RAF BIGGIN HILL
The Other Side
of the Bump

Peter Osborne

From Brooklands to the
Battle of Britain

RAF BIGGIN HILL – The Other Side of the Bump

Peter Osborne

First publication in Great Britain © PJ Osborne 2015

First edition published in 2015 by:

Independent Books
3 Leaves Green Crescent
Keston
Bromley
BR2 6DN
United Kingdom

Tel: 01959 573360

e-mail: mail@indbooks.co.uk

web site: www.indbooks.co.uk

Jacket design and page layout by Independent Books

Printed and bound in Malta by Melita Press

ISBN (13):   978-1-872836-07-2 (Hardback)

ISBN (13):   978-1-872836-12-6 (Paperback)

CONTENTS

Appendices

ILLUSTRATIONS

Page

INTRODUCTION

Most people will associate RAF Biggin Hill with the Battle of Britain, and rightly so, but there is a much, much bigger story to be told. Numerous books exist which plot parts of the story of Biggin Hill, but most focus on World War 2; RAF *Biggin Hill* - Graham Wallace; *Biggin on the Bump* and *Ghosts of Biggin Hill* - Bob Ogley; *Biggin Hill Wing, 1941* - Peter Caygill; *The Road to Biggin Hill* - Vincent Orange; together with a host of mentions in other memoirs and histories. However, very little has been drawn together regarding the experiments and developments which took place at Biggin Hill, virtually all of which would play a key role in the defence of the United Kingdom when war once more came to Europe.

Commencing whilst the First World War raged in France and Belgium, the history of RFC/RAF Biggin Hill was first one of experimental communication. Leaving the mist-shrouded Joyce Green airfield near Dartford, Kent, for the high ground near the area known as Aperfield, in the Parish of Cudham, the Wireless Testing Park continued its work unhampered by the less than equitable conditions on the marshes by the River Thames. This is an oft-recounted story which still bears re-evaluation, as will be revealed later. However, less well researched, but arguably even more important, is the story of the huge War Office site linked to Woolwich Royal Arsenal which was laid out to the south of the airfield. Very little physical evidence of it remains, now mainly buried under an industrial estate and new housing, but deep in old files the fascinating story lies, largely untold. I therefore decided to record as much as I could for posterity before the few people with first-hand knowledge leave us for ever and many records and reports are lost. This is *'The Other Side of the Bump'*

PJO 2015 – Biggin Hill

PROLOGUE

How an area of open farm land in the parish of Cudham, fifteen miles south of London, became the 'most famous fighter station in the world' is a fairly well-trodden path. It began with the need to develop radio communications and grew from there, famously reaching a climax during the Battle of Britain. However the detail of the series of events which put all this in train, and the story of the ground-breaking developments at Biggin Hill is a fascinating account which begins with the embryonic days of flight and the initial grudging acceptance that the aircraft could become the eyes of the army.

The Wright Brothers had made the first flight in a heavier-than-air machine in December 1903 and, just six years later, in 1909, Louis Bleriot made the first channel crossing. Within ten years German bombers were actually able to raid London, such was the rate of development of the aircraft. However, although the employment of early aircraft had, what seems now to be obvious, uses for observing the fall of shot for the artillery, movements of enemy troops and marshalling areas, the British Army generally judged it to be of little practical use.

By the end of the American Civil War, balloons and man-carrying kites were being used for observation, and this was carried forward when war came to Europe, in 1914. However, balloons only offered fixed positions and often fell prey to accurate enemy fire. The first recorded use of an aircraft in a military role was a reconnaissance flight by Capt. Piazza of the Corps Aviazione Esercito (Italian Army Aviation Corps) who flew over the Turkish camp at Azizia on 23 October 1913, during the Italo-Turkish War (1911-12), thus opening a new page in the history of military aviation.

Wireless Telegraphy (Morse)

The advantages of the free roving aircraft were obvious to most but, initially, it required the machine to return to base and for the pilot and/or the observer to report. For more useful and immediate information wireless telegraphy (Morse) was the answer, but for a single seat aircraft this would require the pilot to report via a key strapped to his leg; remembering and forming words in Morse code; whilst flying a very rudimentary aircraft; and at one and the same time being subjected to the attention of German (and sometimes Allied) 'Archie' (anti-aircraft fire) - as well as equally dangerous ground based machine gunners and individual small arms fire. Little wonder the army thought, at least at first, it was of little practical use. The answer, if it could be achieved, would be radio telephony (speech), allowing the pilot or observer free range to be able to report in detail whilst still being able to either pilot the machine or, as an observer, maintain a lookout and possibly engage in defensive return fire.

Brooklands airfield was one of the main centres of flying in Britain; Vickers, Sopwith and AV Roe were based there, and most of their aircraft took their first flights from the Surrey airfield. The development of reliable sets with which airborne wireless experiments began at Brooklands with air-to-ground, ground-to-air telegraphy development between autumn 1911 and spring 1912. The first aircraft to be equipped with a wireless for telegraphy had been a Bristol Boxkite from which messages were received on 27 September 1910, at the Bristol hangar at Larkhill, during the Army's autumn manoeuvres on Salisbury Plain. In June 1914, the first successful air-to-air transmissions and reception was made between two BE2s at a distance of about ten miles.

As the First World War ground on, the first Wireless School was to be set up at Brooklands in November 1915, with courses for six RFC Observers at a time in wireless telegraphy. Their primary role, when they returned to the front, would be the art of artillery spotting and reporting on enemy troop movements. It was quite natural, therefore, that the work on wireless telegraphy would morph into the initial experiments with airborne radio telephony. Captain CE Prince (a Marconi engineer) was seconded from the

Yeomanry to the Royal Flying Corp to assume overall control of the radio experiments and, initially, all went well. Most of the service ground contingent was supplied by the Royal Engineers and more expert help was drafted in from the Marconi Company, which was already a world leader in telegraphy.

Thus it was that Marconi engineers brought their expertise in telegraphy to the challenge of radio telephony. Major General 'Boom' Trenchard, officer commanding the RFC, readily recognised the important role the Corps could play in reconnaissance and also appreciated the inherent difficulties of communicating by Morse from an aircraft in flight. He therefore issued a specification for the development of wireless telephony sets which would be reliable in the hostile vibrating environment of an aircraft; would have a range of at least one mile; and should only have one tuning adjustment. Tasked with a watching brief on the work at Brooklands and the establishment of the Wireless School was one Major HCT Dowding, who was later to make great use of airborne telephony as a component part of his command and control system which was to defeat the Luftwaffe twenty-five years into the future.

Telephony had to be the goal, both for ease of use and rate of delivery of information. Trenchard and Dowding could also see that the aircraft would develop as a weapon of war, both for reconnaissance and, as load carrying capacity increased, the potential to carry ordnance and deliver it with relative accuracy. This would lead to machines being developed for specific roles including 'fighters' that would seek out enemy reconnaissance machines and bombers and shoot them down. Enemy fighters would naturally be engaged by friendly fighters and the kind of air battles that were to become a feature of subsequent wars began. Visionaries like Trenchard and Dowding could see this and also understood that command and control in the air would be vital; effective wireless telephony moved up the agenda.

Devices did exist with which speech could be transmitted by wireless, but only in laboratory conditions. At its core was a 'C' type valve which had been developed by another Marconi engineer on loan to the Government, Captain HJ Round (see note at the end of Chapter One). He had already developed improvements to Bellini-Tosi DF (direction finding) sets which would not only play a significant role in WW1 but later, between the wars, would be vital for the 'Biggin Hill Experiments'. It would be the Round valve that would be the key to successful airborne telephony and, together with Captain Prince at Brooklands, they succeeded in making the first air to ground transmissions at Brooklands in the summer of 1915. But all was not well and change was in the air which would eventually cause a few acres of meadowland in Kent to become RFC Station Biggin Hill.

———————————

CHAPTER ONE

BROOKLANDS

The Army, Marconi, Dowding & Trenchard

The story of RFC/RAF Biggin Hill is inextricably linked to that of the aircraft as a means of observation. The embryonic days of wireless communication from aircraft began at Brooklands, situated near Weybridge, Surrey, about twenty miles south-west of central London. The construction of Brooklands Motor Course began in 1907 and was remarkably innovative. It was built by wealthy landowner Hugh Locke King, essentially the first purpose-built racing circuit in the United Kingdom and rightly claims to be the birthplace of British motor sport. Its heydays as a motor racing venue were during the 1920s/1930s when records were being set and broken by the likes of John Cobb and Malcomb Campell, racing such magnificent machines as the Napier-Railton, Bugattis and supercharged Bentleys. But earlier, because the track enclosed a large open space, and the extraction of performance from engines was an on-site skill, it was natural that rudimentary aircraft were developed and flown there too. Thus it was that the likes of AV Roe (later AVRO), Tommy Sopwith and Harry Hawker set up shop and many famous designs were to take their first flights from the grass field. Later, many of the Hawker Hurricanes and Vickers Wellingtons, which were to form the early central cadre of Fighter and Bomber commands in World War 2, were built at Brooklands.

Crucial to our story is another factor; Marconi's Wireless Telegraph and Signals Company had also set up shop close to Brooklands and, amongst other ground-breaking developments, had started to install radio sets in aircraft. Guglielmo Marconi had come to England in February 1896, aged twenty-one, and in 1897 established his communications company. He was building on the work of Heinrick Hertz (the name Hertz now immortalised in the measurement as the unit of frequency in radio) who had tragically died on New Year's Day 1894. The following year Marconi was able to transmit wireless signals 2.4 km (1.5 mi) and on 27 March 1899, he sent the first short message across the Channel. On 12 December 1901, he reported the reception of a signal from Poldhu in Cornwall to Signal Hill in St John's, Newfoundland, a distance of 3,500 km (2,200 mi). His development of wireless expanded exponentially and the Marconi Company played a significant role in expanding communications with the Imperial Wireless Network by telegraphy (Morse). It was later to play a significant role in the Great War by allowing the Royal Navy, for instance, to keep tabs on the positions of the German High Seas Fleet, Zeppelins and submarines. He had also gained much notoriety in such high profile events as the sinking of the Titanic in April 1912. Marconi gave evidence at the inquest and Britain's Post Master General roundly praised him by saying, 'Those who have been saved, have been saved through one man, Mr Marconi and his marvellous invention.'

Another prominent member of the scientific community, Sir Oliver Lodge, had also taken an interest in electro-magnetic waves, which would involve him in a curious twist of fate. He had also built on the work of late Heinrich Hertz, whom Lodge had met in Berlin in 1881, and on 14 August 1894, Lodge had demonstrated before the British Association in Oxford that electromagnetic waves could cause the deflection of a dot of light produced by an instrument in another room. He also proposed and demonstrated that by using long and short applications of power, a message might be sent by Morse code. Lodge was distracted by other arms of science and gave over much time to researching the paranormal, even becoming involved in bringing leading American medium, Mrs Leonora Piper, to Britain and recording some quite remarkable experiments. He is also recorded as saying that he,

'... didn't pursue the matter of telegraphic application because I was unaware that there would be any demand for this kind of telegraphy.'

However, Marconi, who had little scientific training, single-mindedly forged ahead and became the leading player in the field. However, Lodge did develop his work further and in 1902 he and a colleague, Alexander Muirehead, transmitted a message seven miles to Elmers End, near Beckenham, Kent – the curious twist of fate being that his transmitter aerial, which was erected in Ditch Field, adjacent to Beeche Tree House, West Hill, Cudham, was literally a few hundred metres from the perimeter of what was to become, a few years later, RFC Station - Biggin Hill.

The development of reliable sets, with which airborne wireless experiments could be conducted, continued at Brooklands with air-to-ground/ground-to-air telegraphy developing between autumn 1911 and spring 1912. The first aircraft to be equipped with a wireless for telegraphy had been a Bristol Boxkite from which messages were received on 27 September 1910, at the Bristol hangar at Larkhill, during the Army's autumn manoeuvres on Salisbury Plain. In June 1914, the first successful air-to-air transmissions and reception of telegraphy was made between two BE2s at a distance of about ten miles.

Working with the Army

There was a slow recognition of the potential of aircraft as a method of reconnaissance and artillery observation. Eventually the Committee of Imperial Defence established a sub-committee to consider the question of military aviation in November 1911. Following several meetings the sub-committee reported its findings on 28 February 1912, recommending that a Flying Corps be formed that would consist of a Naval Wing (Royal Naval Air Service - RNAS), a military wing (the Royal Flying Corps - RFC), a central flying school be established (Upavon), and that an aircraft factory should be built (Farnborough). The recommendations were accepted and on 13 April 1912, King George V signed a royal warrant establishing the Royal Flying Corps, and the Air Battalion of the Royal Engineers became the Royal Flying Corps a month later on 13 May.

Within the structure of the Army there are Corps who are support units for the main line regiments, such as the Army Service Corps, Medical Corps, Tank Corps etc; over and above these are the major Army Corps like the First and Second Corps which made up the British Expeditionary Force (BEF). The RFC and RNAS were initially independent but morphed into the Royal Air Force in 1918, making the third independent service alongside the Navy and Army. However in the years leading up to WW1 the RFC was very much a junior partner to the Senior Service and the Army. Communications, or probably more correctly, 'Signals', was part of the Army's stock in trade and with the Royal Engineers, the Royal Artillery, Royal Military Academy (which didn't move to Sandhurst until 1939) and the Royal Ordinance Factory (better known locally as 'The Arsenal'), were all located at Woolwich, to the south-east of London (actually in Kent at that time); it would be there that the development of equipment began. To improve radio communications, both using telegraphy (Morse) and, later, telephony (speech), the Royal Engineers began developing equipment in conjunction with Marconi's engineers at Brooklands. Equipment was assembled in the Royal Engineers camp on Woolwich Common and then transferred by road to Brooklands for testing, modification and evaluation.

With the coming of the First World War all technical developments were stepped up and the potential for the aircraft to play a significant role in the field of observation, using wireless telegraphy, was soon recognised. However, so were the shortcomings of the requirement to communicate using Morse code as it was both demanding of the pilots or observers and slow to deliver; telephony, if it could be achieved, was the answer. The process of transmitting voice communication was not new; a Canadian, Reginald Aubrey Fessenden, is generally recognized as the first to actually transmit the sound of the human voice without wires. Working at Rock Point, Maryland, he experimented with a high frequency spark transmitter and successfully transmitted speech a distance of one mile (1.6 km) on 23 December 1900. The sound quality was very poor but it was a beginning on which he built, making the first general broadcast on 24 December 1906. By the start of World War I the science had advanced considerably, but the creation of a radio set that could perform adequately in the hostile environment of an aircraft was still something of a challenge.

Experiments at Brooklands continued apace with numerous sets designed, tested, modified and eventually scrapped. Microphones were one of the key issues, either being too sensitive or barely recording the speech of the user. They depended on the vibration of carbon granules to generate the tiny variations in current which could be decoded by a receiver as speech. However they were by nature extremely delicate and did not respond favourably to the vibration, background noise and changes in temperature inherent in a rudimentary open cockpit aircraft. The aerials, too, were a constant problem being a maximum length of 150 feet of copper wire, weighted at one end, which had to be reeled out by the pilot or

Test aircraft with weighted aerial extended (Royal Artillery Heritage Trust)

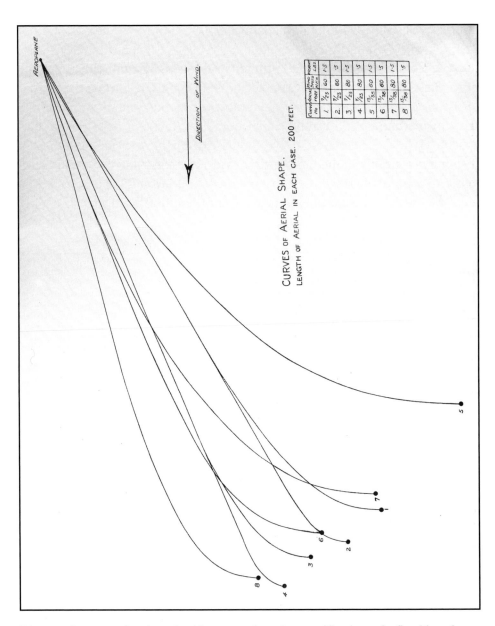

Diagram demonstrating the scientific approach to the specification of a fixed length aerial (200 ft) where the variables are the diameter of the wire, the speed of the wind and the mass of the weight attached to the end of the aerial.

observer once airborne, but which sometimes became detached and were lost, or, more often, the crew forgot to reel them in and the trees around Brooklands became festooned with lengths of wire which grumbling junior ranks were tasked with recovering.

HCT Dowding

Hugh Caswall Tremenheere Dowding was born a Scot in the small village of Moffat, south of Edinburgh in April 1882. He grew up in there and took the first stage of his education at St Ninian's school, of which his father, Arthur John, was headmaster. From St Ninian's, Dowding followed the family tradition and, age 14, moved to Wiltshire and was enrolled in Winchester College. He had travelled alone from Scotland and remained at the college for four years with little routine contact with his family. The young Dowding had not really excelled in any particular field and wasn't anything like the sports all-rounder his father had been. He had thought he wanted to be an engineer but, in the absence of any clear way ahead, he applied for and was enrolled in the Royal Military Academy, Woolwich in 1899.

With the outbreak of the Second Boer War (18 October 1899) the course at the Academy was shortened to one year and Dowding was commissioned, age 18, as a second Lieutenant in the Royal Garrison Artillery in August 1900, having failed to win the commission he wanted in the Royal Engineers, which he realistically blamed on a lack of application on his own part. Second Lieutenant Dowding sailed for his first posting in Gibraltar and then, in 1901, by ship to Ceylon. There he began to spread his wings, proving to be a good natural shot, bringing down birds in flight, and also finding a good seat on polo ponies. In those days of Empire the ability to put in a spirited game of polo was a social requirement of any ambitious subaltern, much like playing rugby or having an excellent golf handicap does the young officers of today no harm.

Addressing his career prospects he applied for the Mountain Artillery, but before this could be processed he was transferred to Hong Kong. In May 1902, he was promoted to full Lieutenant and enjoyed the very full life on offer; polo, horse racing, sailing, picnics in the New Territories and even bought his own pony which he named Panjandram (a person who has or claims to have a great deal of authority or influence) because he thought that, although the animal looked good, he hadn't a hope of distinguishing himself. However, Dowding was somewhat surprised when he rode him in his first race and won by a comfortable margin.

In the spring of 1904, Dowding joined the mountain battery and was shipped out to Rawalpindi in the Punjab. For the next six years he enjoyed life with the British Raj, which was at a high point. Several postings followed and in the end he was to serve ten years overseas before finally being recommended for a position at the staff college, Camberley.

Whilst at Camberley, Dowding was put in charge of a syndicate and had at his disposal six theoretical aircraft and tasked with checking if Grantham, Lincolnshire (135 miles away), was in 'enemy hands'. He put forward the solution that the aircraft would fly north and take a look. When challenged as to how they would navigate and find Grantham he simply suggested that they would follow railway lines. The outcome of the exercise is unknown but it seems it was enough to pique Dowding's interest in the new science of aviation and he decided to learn to fly, and where more appropriate than at Brooklands, just sixteen miles away from Camberley.

The flying school was run by Vickers and the aircraft of choice was the Bristol Boxkite, a reasonably reliable and stable platform on which to learn the rudiments of aviation. After a remarkably short course, consisting of one hour and forty minutes flying, he was granted Royal Aero Club Pilot's Certificate No. 711. This was awarded on the same day as he passed out from Camberley in the new rank of Captain, on 20 December 1913. Although the training for his Pilot's certificate had been brief, and contained little solo time, it was enough for him to take the three month RFC course at Upavon in early 1914.

Now in his early thirties, Dowding had earned himself the sobriquet 'Stuffy', probably because he didn't eagerly enter into the round of social occasions offered by his peers at Camberley, and he keep himself to himself with only a close circle of friends and acquaintances. However he was far from boring; a very confident skier, experienced horseman and an excellent shot, he enjoyed individual sports but could hardly be described as a natural team player. He had also begun to carve out a reputation for speaking his mind, irrespective of the apparent status of authority, and also for not suffering fools gladly.

With the beginning of the First World War there was a frantic effort to get men and materiel to France in support of the British Expeditionary Force. Dowding was tasked with martialling four squadrons at Dover for the flight over the Channel, then to make his way around the country scooping up the lame ducks that hadn't made it to the point of departure. He constantly petitioned Major General 'Boom' Trenchard, who was Officer Commanding the Military Wing at Farnborough, Hants, to have him posted to France. In October he got his wish, joining No. 6 Squadron (motto - *'Oculi exercitus'* - 'The Eyes of the Army') at Farnborough, ready to deploy to Bruges, Belgium, on 6 October, three days later moving on to St Omer, 20 miles (35 km) south-east of Calais.

Initially flying as an observer, he gained experience of front line aviation and survived two crashes on landing. On 29 November 1914, the fledgling RFC was established into two wings, one based with the First Army Corps at St Omer, the other in support of the Second Army Corps, and with this consolidation Dowding resumed his flying career as a pilot and was posted to No. 9 Squadron on Christmas morning. In January 1915, he was made up to Flight Commander on the first 'wireless squadron' and his link with airborne communications had been forged.

The Officer Commanding the squadron was an Australian, Major Herbert Musgrave, who seemed often prone to quirky behaviour. He had insisted that the wings of their aircraft, which had been operating for months in the open, were still serviceable in the face of advice from the senior ground staff that the linen covering was slack, and therefore not generating maximum lift or affording the most efficient manoeuvrability. When Musgrave went on leave, leaving Dowding in charge, he ordered the immediate replacement of the wings. On his return Musgrave apparently flew into a rage which Dowding weathered with his customary immaculate calm. News of Musgrave's behaviour reached Army HQ and he was recalled to the Army; as a consequence Dowding was promoted to Major and stepped up to his first command. [Musgrave was later to be killed by a fragment of a rifle grenade in 1918 when leading a night patrol – aged 42!]

As the war moved on, the original No. 9 Squadron was broken up and reformed at Brooklands as the 'Wireless Experimental Establishment'. Dowding, having served on the front line as both an observer and a pilot, could see the potential of improved communications and enthusiastically embraced his new role. Captain CE Prince (another Marconi engineer) was seconded from the Yeomanry to the Royal Flying Corp to assume overall control of the radio experiments and, initially, all went well. Prince resurrected a set which depended upon the use of a single Round valve (invented by Captain Round – see note at the end of the chapter). The team worked throughout the spring and early summer of 1915 to convert the delicate laboratory equipment into something more suited to the rigours of flight.

Recorded in a paper written by Majors Orme and Prince entitled, 'History of RFC Wireless From The Outbreak of War' is the following:

'On the formation of No. 9 Squadron at Brooklands under Major HCT Dowding in April, 1915, Lieutenant R Orme was posted as wireless officer to the Squadron. Within a few days of this, Lietenant CE Prince, an ex-member of the Marconi Research Staff, who since the outbreak of war had been in charge of a wireless section of the Westmoreland and Cumberland Yeomanry, consisting of two cavalry stations, (of which he had been one of the the designers) with personnel, were lent to the Royal Flying Corps and attached to No. 9 Squadron. Shortly afterwards, the stations, with NCOs and men, were transferred to a home defence unit, Lieut Prince remaining at Brooklands with the RFC to which he was subsequently formally attached. In addition to these two officers, a small section of NCOs and men, including Sergeant (now Captain) LE Taylor, RE, came from the first No 9 Squadron at St Omer, and were incorporated in the new No. 9 Squadron at Brooklands.
This Squadron had now a special wireless flight with the technical personnel above mentioned, and under Major Dowding's energetic guidance, a period of great wireless activity was inaugurated, which was the genesis of all subsequent aircraft wireless work in the RFC at home'.

However the War Office were less than forthcoming in terms of funding or equipment and Dowding and Prince were, on occasion, forced to take matters into their own hands. Prince recorded that he and Dowding began visiting Marconi's offices in Aldwych, and whilst Dowding chatted amiably to the storeman and regaled him with stories of front line daring-do, Prince would ferret around on the shelves and drop vital components, especially valves, into his pockets, later referring to these nefarious activities as a simple re-allocation of stores. Using these components his team were able to build a set of considerably less weight, which was more robust and had a much increased range. He wrote, 'It seemed almost beyond hope to achieve really practical wireless telephony from an aeroplane, but the difficulties have been overcome, and the new set is by no means a toy, or only of scientific interest. A new and amazing power is conferred by it.'

In spite of these leaps forward, or possibly because of them, the atmosphere at Brooklands continued to be less than convivial. Most of the service ground contingent was supplied by the Royal Engineers and more expert help was drafted in from the Marconi Company, already a world leader in telegraphy. The 'regulars' of the Royal Engineers saw the Marconi men as 'Hostilities-Only Commissions' and found their lack of understanding of service protocols and discipline unsettling. Equally, Capt. Prince and the other Marconi men found the plodding unimaginative approach of the Army frustrating and limited in scope. In a paper by Major Orme (who was effectively in charge of the experimental unit), and Captain Prince the '… undefined opposition to experimental work at Brooklands was becoming evident in the War Office.' The decision was made to move all the research and development of wireless to Woolwich where the massive arsenal complex was at the cutting edge of weapon and ancillary equipment development. Following the move, new equipment was transported the fifty or so miles to Brooklands for air testing, but it was less than satisfactory.

In July 1915, Dowding was posted away from the wireless work to take command of No. 16 Squadron, at that time based at Merville. As the First World War ground on, the first Wireless School was set up at Brooklands in November 1915, with courses for six RFC Observers at a time in wireless telegraphy. When they returned to the front their primary role would be the art of artillery spotting and reporting on enemy troop movements using well established telegraphy. Also, in the summer of 1915, Trenchard was promoted to Brigadier-General and placed in charge of the RFC in France. He could see the importance of communication, and especially appreciated the value of aircraft in the role of the eyes of the army, and was later to issue a specification for new and more effective radio equipment for aircraft.

However, outside of this, the niggling disputes at Brooklands continued and, following the move of the workshops to Woolwich, the RFC moved to Joyce Green airfield, situated close to the Thames on the salt marshes, immediately north of Dartford.

In July 1916 Dowding assumed command of No. 16 Squadron. Above is their airfield at Beaupré Farm, La Gorgue, east of Merville. (National Archive)

Note:

Captain HJ Round MC was working for the Marconi Company when his work came to the attention of the War Office. At the outbreak of war he was seconded to the intelligence service where the focus was on his work on direction finding. On 30 May 1916, wireless intercepts indicated a large volume of traffic from a key German warship at Wilhelmshaven. The improved DF equipment, powered by the Round Valve, then clearly indicated that ships were preparing to get underway, which was enough to mobilise the Grand Fleet. Since the beginning of the war the Fleet had been trying to engage the *Hochseeflotte* (German High Seas Fleet) but had been faced with a cat-and-mouse game, which usually resulted in the German ships steaming out of range before the Fleet could be formed up. Now, however, all indica-

Captain HC Round MC

tions were that the *Hochseeflotte* was heading out into the North Sea and the Home Fleet would be ready. On 31 May and 1 June battle was joined off Jutland and was the only major fleet action of WW1. Captain Round's part in this was not generally known until well after the cessation of hostilities.

Round went on to invent and improve numerous items of equipment (including submarine detecting ASDIC – later called Sonar), eventually holding some 117 patents. His eldest son, John, was to be killed flying a fighter with the RAF in the Far East, just six weeks before the end of the war. Round died in 1966, aged 85.

CHAPTER TWO

JOYCE GREEN AIRFIELD 1911 - 1919

The Wireless Testing Park

Following the move to Woolwich there was only one airfield in the vicinity, Joyce Green, near Dartford, which nestled beside the Thames where the River Darent joins it as a tributory. It had been opened by Vickers, in 1911, to air test aircraft built at their Crayford plant and occupied about 110 acres of salt marsh which had been part of Franks Farm. As it was already in use by Vickers it was quickly adopted by the Royal Flying Corps as part of the urgently required defences of London when the Zeppelin raids began.

Just back from the riverbank stood the Long Reach Tavern, a solitary public house, which catered for the boatmen of the Thames and a few farmhands. Isolated and close to the river, it inevitably became the focus of tales of smuggling and other nefarious dealing, as well as regular bouts of bare-knuckle boxing. With the appearance of the RCF, in 1915, part of the pub became a wet canteen for the NCOs and some of the upper rooms were used as sleeping quarters for the Senior NCOs. All other personnel were accommodated in huts and tents, with hangars, workshops and supply stores erected along the line of the river, close to the Tavern. An Officers' Mess was opened towards the southern end of the airfield, on the east side of Joyce Green Lane, about where the remains of Joseph Wells firework factory stand today. Vickers hangars were similarly located to the south of the airfield and aircraft built at Crayford continued to be assembled and tested despite the invasion of the RFC.

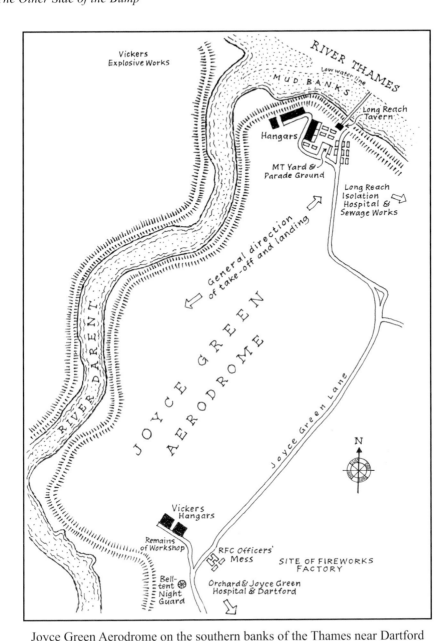

Joyce Green Aerodrome on the southern banks of the Thames near Dartford

Joyce Green - Thought to be Pay Parade. To the right MT Sheds and in
the background the Long Reach Tavern. To the left of that can be seen sails of
Thames Barges illustrating how close the airfield was to the river.
Below: The parade disperses.

(Kent County Libraries, Registration & Archives - Dartford Library)

The Wireless Testing Park arrived from Brooklands and commenced test
equipment assembled at Woolwich, however the limitations of the airfield
were soon apparent. Being low down it was not ideal for wireless transmissions and, being built on salt marsh and criss-crossed with boarded over
drainage ditches, inevitably led to a lot of ground fog and mist which obviously restricted a full flying programme. It was because of this that, in late

1916, Lieutenants Furnival (a Marconi engineer seconded to the Army) and Hansard (RFC) set off to find an alternative airfield. Several popular stories impinge on this moment in time because their search was to lead to the development of RFC Station - Biggin Hill.

No. 10 Training Squadron RFC DE H2. Wreckage of a flying accident being recovered from the Sewage Works.

(Kent County Libraries, Registration & Archives - Dartford Library)

Above: Airco DH 5 Number A9437 being recovered from the Thames.
Below: No. 10 Training Squadron aircraft on the roadside looking east.
(Kent County Libraries, Registration & Archives - Dartford Library)

Above: No. 10 Training Squadron RFC FE 8. Hangars in the left background back onto the Darenth embankment. (Kent County Libraries, Registration & Archives - Dartford Library)

Left: Some of the graves of airmen killed at Joyce Green. Watling Street Cemetery, Dartford.

In 'RAF Biggin Hill' by Graham Wallace (pages 15 & 16), it is recorded that Lieutenant Hansard had relatives in Limpsfield, and that he and Furnival set out from Joyce Green to visit one Sunday afternoon. Passing a large open field in Aperfield, in the Parish of Cudham, they stopped to consider it as a potential airfield. It was some 550 feet above sea level, indeed they could see the general area of Joyce Green from where they stood, and its elevated position would allow excellent wireless range and it should be relatively free of fog. On further investigation they found a large house just south of the field named Koonowla, which they estimated would make an excellent mess for their fellow officers.

It is a perfectly plausible story, and probably contains much of the truth; Hansard may have had relatives in Limpsfield but no proof of that has come to light, and the chance discovery is, in my view, unlikely. Certainly the two of them set off from Joyce Green on the orders of Major Orme (Officer Commanding the Wireless Testing Park) to find an alternative location; relations with Army Signals were still less than harmonious, and the increased use of the field for training by the RFC may have led to further difficulties.

The next possibility in terms of the 'discovery' of what was to become Biggin Hill Aerodome is enshrined in local oral folk history which would have it that a large meadow, which was part of Cudham Lodge Farm, was designated as an Emergency Landing Ground (ELG) in about 1912. Because of this the farmer was limited in the type of crops he could grow; nothing that required deep ploughing of the field or excessively tall crops – so basically grass for hay. This seems to be underscored by an article by Michael Page in Volume Seven, Number 12 (1986) of 'Bygone Kent', which records that:

'In 1915 the Earl of Stanhope, who owned much of the land, offered the seventy-five acre meadow which was part of Cuham Lodge Farm to the War Office as an Emergency Night Landing Ground (ENLG).'

In response to this Mr GW Smith of Bromley Common provided some first-hand information published in a subsequent edition of Bygone Kent. I n 1987, he wrote:

'From my own recollection as a young lad then living a few miles distant, there are earlier details to be recorded. The nearby farmhouse was called Cudham Lodge and the surrounding land owned by Lord Stanhope of Chevening, his tenant being Mr John Westcott.

'I believe it was in 1912, when the Royal Engineers had a Balloon Section on Salisbury Palin, that a Farman Biplane connected with the exercises developed engine trouble over the area of the Kent and Surrey border. The pilot saw the large 70-acre field of Cudham Lodge Farm and, after making a safe landing, made his way to Mr Westcott at the farmhouse who then drove him in his pony and trap to Westerham, where the pilot was able to report back to his base.

'The next day a lorry arrived with an officer and mechanics; when the necessary repairs had been carried out the aircraft took off. The officer, however, noted the value of the high elevation of this large fairly flat field and enquired of Mr Westcott if some arrangement might be made to use it for emergency landings.

'At about this time my family firm of Builders, Wm Smith & Sons of Bromley Common, were working at Cudham Lodge Farm. The Royal Engineers contacted Mr Westcott proposing the erection of a small store shed in his field at the rear of The Kings Arms public house at Leaves Green. This was agreed and the sections of the shed were duly delivered to Hayes Station, which the builder, Wm Smith, was to collect and erect in the corner of 70-acre field for the storage of spares etc.'

GW 'Gee' Smith commanded the local platoon of the Local Defence Volunteers (LDV), which later became Home Guard. One of their roles was the defence of the northern perimeter of the airfield (by then RAF Biggin Hill).

It therefore seems very likely that Hansard and Furnival were making a deliberate visit to an area known to them, either on charts of the time or in their pilot's notes (there's no point in designating a area as an ELG if pilots don't know about it!). Besides which, we have the likelihood that

Hansard and/or his brother pilots could have seen the site at Cudham Lodge Farm from the air as they transited between Brooklands and Joyce Green. Biggin Hill stands out on the North Downs and would have easily been seen, about eight miles south of a direct track to and from Joyce Green. Precision navigation was still in its infancy and a small error in heading or a stronger than expected wind from the north would easily have seen them overhead the site of the ELG – they may even investigated it because of its designation; ideally if you've got to land because of an emergency it would be better to be familiar with the field if possible.

There are, therefore, two references to the meadow or field in question being designated for use for emergency landing, and the possibility that this might have brought an investigation from the air. It is most likely that this is was what brought Hansard and Furnival to Aperfield, Hansard to look at it from a pilot's perspective, and Furnival from the view of it becoming a key position for wireless research.

By the summer of 1916 real pressure was on to develop both radio communications as well as DF (Direction Finding) and the limitations of Joyce Green had been well and truly exposed thought the preceding autumn and winter. It continued in use and the training element expanded although it was not a popular airfield, being situated primarily on marshland. Air Vice Marshal Gould Lee wrote:

'To use this waterlogged field for testing now and then was reasonable and to take advantage of it as an emergency landing ground for Home Defence forces was credible, but to employ it as a flying training station was folly and as a Camel (i.e. Sopwith Camel aeroplane) training station was lunacy. A pupil taking off with a choked or failing engine had to choose, according to wind direction, between drowning in the Thames (half a mile wide at this point), crashing into the Vickers TNT (explosives) Works, sinking into a vast sewage farm, killing himself and numerous patients in a large isolation hospital, being electrocuted in an electrical station with acres of pylons and cables; or trying to turn and get back to the aerodrome. Unfortunately, many pupils confronted with disaster tried the last course and span to their deaths.'

The decision was made and the move to Biggin Hill began, leaving Joyce Green as a fighter station with some training responsibilities. However, with the end of the war came the end of the demand for huge numbers of military aircraft and Vickers were slow to embrace the building of passenger aircraft; although they did make an enclosed version of the Vimy. The Crayford assembly plant was turned over to the production of sewing machines and there was little traffic at Joyce Green. In May 1915 Beddington Aerodrome had been opened to form part of the defence ring around London and was situated south of Croydon on Plough Lane. It was already preferable to Joyce Green with its unpredictable flying conditions and would continue to bleed traffic away from the Thames-side airfield. Later, Waddon Aerodrome opened on the opposite side of the Plough Lane to serve the National Air-craft Factory No. 1. The two aerodromes were to be combined to form Croy-don airport which was opened in 1920, by which time the necessity for Joyce Green as an airfield had long passed.

Joyce Green Airfield today

In 1919, with the closing of 'surplus' airfields, the RAF left Joyce Green and, with the post-war wind-down of aircraft production at Vickers Crayford works, the airfield was handed back to the original land owner; however some private flying continued. It is unclear how many of the buildings were left in situ by the RAF and Vickers, but a painting of the Long Reach Tavern, which was executed in 1935, seems to show large hangar-like structures to the rear of the pub. However, a photograph of the area in the 1953 floods shows only the pub surrounded by water and Long Reach Hospital awash. Today there is evidence of the past but it's hard to find. Following the '53 floods, the pub was abandoned and became derelict, finally being set on fire to by vandals. It was demolished (as was Long Reach Hospital) as part of the reconstruction work on the banks of the Thames which saw a much higher riverbank erected on the land side of the existing. This new construc-tion covered some of the area where the RFC/RAF buildings once stood but, for instance, the metalled roadway which once passed in front of the Motor Transport Section can still be found, although nature is creeping across from both sides, intent on obliterating it. Other large blocks of concrete, some pieces of granite lintel, bricks and a few substantial baulks of timber can be found which might have been associated with building on the airfield but it is far from conclusive.

At the south end of the former airfield there are a few derelict buildings which appear to be used as cattle shelters and have a brick-built chimney, low walls and the rusting remains of military pattern steel framed windows. They are in the right position to have been administration offices or small workshops to the rear of Vickers hangars. To the immediate north of these remains lies a clearly artificially flat area of grazing which could well have been the apron. There are also some large concrete blocks which may have formed the corners of a ramp which was dug out when the first Vimy arrived for assembly and testing; it was too tall to fit in the hangar and the floor had to be dug out. In 1911, when the hangars were built, such relatively huge aircraft were not even sketches on designers' pads.

It is easy to stand on the road near the north-easterly corner of the airfield and imagine the motors being run up prior to the diagonal run across the airfield (into the prevailing south-westerly wind), and the popping and banging as returning aircraft came in to land, carburation lean and throttles closed, just clearing Joyce Green Lane before bumping across the coarse grass. On a pleasant day it is easy to see why it was made an airfield but, on an average damp, cold, winter day it's equally easy to see why it had its limitations (turning 'finals to land' over the middle of the Thames being but one!). If you wish to visit the site it is easily appreciated without leaving the roadway and venturing onto private land. It is also best to go on a weekend when both the Nomads Model Flying Club is operating (on part of the old airfield) and the shot-gunners are meeting at their club. This ensures that the barriers across Joyce Green Lane are open, and one can drive down as far as the gun club. If you ask politely they will let you park, and even serve you a civil cuppa upon your return from the river bank. Access is then over a stile-like attachment to the Environment Agency barrier across Joyce Green Lane and a fifteen- twenty minute walk to the site of the camp.

The lower part of the war memorial plaque in St Alban's Church, Dartford,
showing the names of the 29 military pilots who lost their lives at Joyce Green.
A full list is recorded in Appendix 1.

There is also St Albans Church, St Albans Road, Dartford, which was
the parish church at the time the airfield was in operation. Again there is no
record of the exact association with the airfield, whether church parades
were held at the church, or if the incumbent vicar presided over a Sunday
Service at the airfield. What remains is an extension to the parish war
memorial plaque inside the church which records the twenty-nine young
aircrew that lost their lives in the parish. Some of their graves are set out
together in Watling Street Cemetery, but others were interred closer to their
homes.

Of the non-service flyers that lost their lives, no complete record or
memorial has, as yet, has been discovered. What is recorded is the first of
what is said to be a 'long line of fatalities'. It took place on the afternoon of
January 13, 1913, when a Monoplane No. 6 which had been converted to a
biplane was to be flown. It was piloted by a Mr Leslie McDonald with mechanic Harry English as passenger, taking off at 3.30 pm and heading north
over the Thames on what was scheduled as a routine test flight. Those
watching said later that the machine seemed to have difficulty in gaining
height and at no time exceeded much over a hundred feet. It then apparently
turned west along the river and descended, under control, onto the surface

of the water where it remained afloat for some minutes. One man, thought to be Harry English, was seen to strike out for the Kentish shore but no movement was observed from the pilot before the machine sank; soon afterwards the swimmer was also lost from view. An intensive search was mounted buy the local boatmen but neither body was ever found.

Joyce Green has its own history and what is recorded here is enough to place it in the development of RAF Biggin Hill. It is tempting to expand on this small but important chapter of aviation history but it would only serve to distract us from our purpose.

CHAPTER THREE

THE BIRTH OF A LEGEND 1916 – 1918

RFC Station Biggin Hill comes to life

Following the decision to move from Joyce Green to Biggin Hill the necessary purchase orders and leases we prepared and signed. The use of the 'Red House' (Koonowla) as an Officers' Mess had proved to be one of the more difficult obstacles as it had been set up to provide a convalescent home for 'poor' children under the auspices of the Chelsea Hospital for Sick Children. In the end the War Office had to call upon the exigencies of the Defence of the Realm Act (1914) to evict them.

So the preparation for the meadow on Cudham Lodge Farm to become RCF Station – Biggin Hill continued. The autumn and beginning of the winter of 1916 was both cold and wet and the most used areas of the new field were reduced to lakes of mud into which tools were lost, boots were pulled off and vehicles became stuck. But gradually the Bessonneau hangars ('hangar' – French for 'barn') were erected and all manner of packing crates and spare material pressed into service to make temporary offices and workshops. Most accommodation was under canvass, except for the officers who had already populated the vacated 'Red House'.

When the rain stopped, the ground froze and then the wind direction changed to the north and north-east which brought snow to the high ground at Biggin Hill to add to the misery of the 'troops'. The first aircraft was due

An RE 7 at Biggin Hill, 1917. The RE 7 was by most accounts a singularly
poor aircraft, thus probably relegated to experimental radio work.

to arrive from Joyce green on 1 January but the cold conditions had precipitated fog along the Thames and Joyce Green was 'socked-in'. Therefore it
was not until 2 January, 1917, that an RE 7, piloted by Lieutenant Dickie,
with Air Mechanic Chadwick touched down at Biggin Hill with little idea
of the history that would follow their first landing. As it was they were show-
ered with slushy snowballs before the aircraft could be man-handled in the
relative shelter of the canvass and wood Bessonneau.

By the second week in February most of the transfer and issue of new
equipment was complete and a new address was promulgated in Routine
Orders by Major Orme:

Biggin Hill Aerodrome, Near Westerham, Kent.
(Later to be officially confirmed as Royal Flying Corps Station - Biggin Hill).

Construction of new buildings and workshops continued as the research and
development work of the Wireless Testing Park continued. This was not
only aimed at further developing the potential of telephony covering air-to-

An unknown officer apparently examining a camera. Behind him to the right is a Bessenneau hangar, with rolled canvass and a mass of building materials beside it. The first permanent buildings are under construction in the background. (RAF Museum)

ground and ground-to-air but to conquer that which had evaded all trials, the thus far illusive air-to-air wireless telephony. Equipment was built at Woolwich and brought up to Biggin Hill for testing with failure or rejection being the usual result. It was frustrating that sets would work perfectly on a test bench but in the rough and tumble of aviation they were soon overwhelmed. Sometimes it is best to go back to basics and it was decided to try the earlier set designed by Prince, using the Round valve. Literally packed in cotton wool the set and microphone were installed in a test aircraft and to everyone's amazement and delight transmissions from an orbiting aircraft were received.

However it was air-to-air transmission and reception that was the prize and, following the installation of the ground set in another Sopwith, the two aircraft took off on a calm July evening, one piloted by Lieutenant Peck with Lieutenant Furnival in the back cockpit, and the second piloted by

Lieutenant Hansard with Lieutenant Andrews as his rear. Levelling out toward Sevenoaks the copper aerials were reeled out and the two aircraft drifted apart to create a meaningful range whilst still remaining in visual contact. Andrews began a standard test message with numbers to ten, followed by the days of the week. It had been agreed that Furinval's aircraft would dip its wings if the transmission was hear and as Furnival tuned the set across the waveband he suddenly picked up Andrew's transmission, almost lost in the interference from the engine's magnetos. Leaning forward he tapped Peck on the shoulder and gave him the thumbs up. Peck immediately rocked the joy stick from side to side and Hansard responded. Widening the gap between the two aircraft the transmission was still weak but clear and it was with great excitement that the two crews reeled in their aerials and landed back at Biggin Hill.

Left Lt Hansard, centre Lt Peck, right Lt Furnival. A careful examination of Furnival's right hand will reveal what looks like a Champagne flute, offering the tantalizing prospect that this was the day they made the transmission.

A similar picture as the last, with Sopwiths to the rear. Left is Lt Peck and extreme right
is Lt Furnival,but the other three are unknown. Two are pilots, therefore one could be
Lt Andrews who flew the second aircraft in the successful experiment.
(RAF Museum)

Then it was just a question of repeating the experiment and developing
equipment, robust enough for airmen to take to war. The responsibility for
this fell to the Experimental Wireless Telegraphy Section, Royal Engineers
which had moved to Woolwich Dockyard in 1914 (from Chatham) and, in
1916, moved to Woolwich Common with 150 staff to become the Signals
Experimental Establishment (SEE), under the Chief Experimental Officer
(CEO) Col. AH Bagnold. It was soon to move once more, this time to Biggin
Hill, to focus the efforts of improved radio in one place for, primarily, the
RFC, and secondarily for general use for the army. More and more sections
of the research were being transferred to Biggin Hill, populating the War
Office site to the south of the active airfield, appropriately known as South
Camp. Eventually some 1200 personnel would occupy this site (now largely
lost under the industrial estate and housing) but was certainly large enough
to warrant having its own hospital and mortuary, several messes and some

married quarters.

At one and the same time improvements were being made in ground to air and air to ground communications and as part of this the manor house known as Aperfield Court, about a mile further south of the airfield, was taken over and a powerful radio transmitter installed. This would, in the fullness of time, become part of an embryonic command and control system which was to develop, some 22 years later, into the network which would control the defence of the UK.

Aperfield Court, which was demolished in 1920, once housed a radio transmitter for Biggin Hill. The Cedar tree to the left still stands beside Aperfield Road as an indicator of the original site of the court. (John Nelson)

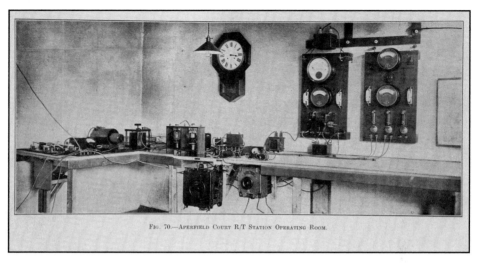

FIG. 70.—APERFIELD COURT R/T STATION OPERATING ROOM.

Aperfield Court Radio Operations Room. Taken from the Report of the Wireless Experimental Establishment, Biggin Hill, Kent. 1918.
(National Archive)

The Wireless Experimental Establishment Biggin Hill, 1918. At this time there was in excess of 400 people working at the establishment, both military and civil.
(RAF Museum)

PREFACE.

At the opening of the year Experimental Work was being carried out at three separate establishments, viz., W.E.E., Biggin Hill, Signals Experimental Establishment, Woolwich, and the R.N.A.S. Experimental Establishment at Cranwell. The Air Force work of these three Establishments was co-ordinated at Biggin Hill on the formation of the third Service in April 1918.

This Report deals with new apparatus produced or brought into service during the year. Accounts of the work in Radio-telephony and Direction Finding are given, and finally various tests and investigations are described.

The Preface from the The Wireless Experimental Establishment Biggin Hill Report, 1918, which sets out the objectives and confirms that all reasearch was centralised at Biggin Hill in April, 1918. (National Archive)

FIG. 15.—TELEPHONE, WIRELESS, AIRCRAFT, MARK III. SET RECEIVING.

Mk III Radio set developed and built at Biggin Hill. (National Archive)

The war still raged along the Western Front and the German *Luftstreikräfte* (Imperial Airforce) continued to raid England. With the continuing success of the RFC and RNAS in shooting down Zeppelins, fewer raids were mounted using the lighter than air machines. The bulk of the raids therefore fell to the heavier than air machines, and although their campaign did not add up to a huge offensive on the scale of WW 2, there were instances of significant damage to both military and civilian targets; probably one of the worst being the raid on Folkestone on Friday, 25 May, 1917. There, some 76 civilians were killed and 96 injured (mainly in Tontine Street) and at Shorncliffe Barracks where 18 soldiers were killed and 90 wounded.

The German airmen were later to claim that they had been unable to bomb their primary targets in Essex and had elected to sweep inland and attack Shornecliffe Barracks and Folkestone Harbour before making the Channel crossing, north-east towards northern France and Belgium. This is not unlikely because there were large concentrations of troops in the barracks above Folkestone and Hythe and the vast majority of troops were shipped across to France from Folkestone harbour. However, bombing from between 14 & 20,000 feet went disastrously wrong and at least one bomb which fell in Tontine Street, killed 16 men, 28 women and 27 children who had been out shopping and socialising, preparing for the Whitsun Bank Holiday which would have fallen on the following Monday.

Although there was a huge demand for aircraft to feed war machine in the Western Front it became more and obvious that something had to be done to beef-up the defence of the realm. Joyce Green with its less than ideal flying conditions was pretty much up to capacity as a training and Camel conversion unit, as well as flying defensive patrols. Biggin Hill was an obvious choice to accept more aircraft and to become an operational fighter airfield.The first Squadron to come to 'The Bump' was No. 141 Squadron:

No. 141 Squadron RFC/RAF 1918-1919.
Motto. *Caedimus noctu* 'We Slay by Night'
Formed 1st January, 1918, at Rochford, Essex.
OC Maj. Philip Babington MC.

The squadron was formed from 'A' Flight of No. 61 Squadron, flying SE5A's and Sopwith Pups. The squadron moved to Biggin Hill on 9 February, 1918, the first resident squadron. In the middle of February some more personnel and aircraft (BE12s) were transferred from No. 78 Squadron.

At 00:30hrs, 20 May, Turner (pilot) and Barwise (observer) picked up Gotha GV 979/16 over South Ash. Turner positioned his aircraft below and behind the Gotha. When the enemy filled his gunsight he signalled Barwise to fire. The first burst hit the port engine which must have immediately lost power because the aircraft was reported as yawing violently. Barwise fired two more bursts into the fuselage and starboard wings and then lost contact. The Gotha crashed between Frinsted and Harrietsham at about 00:45hrs.

At 00:25hrs Maj J.F. Sowrey of No. 143 Squardron had fired 2 double drums at the same aircraft, possibly wounding the pilot but the victory was given to No. 141 Squadron based on the testimony of the German gunner, the only survivor. Turner and Barwise each receiving the Distinguished Flying Cross.

Another aspect of this first kill was to put in train major changes in aerial warfare tactics but was to be the only practical demonstration during the First World War. As mentioned earlier a powerful transmitter and receiver had been set up in Aperfield Court by Lieutenant Furnival. Telephone lines had also been brought in from the Coast Guard, established anti-aircraft gun sites and the Metropolitan Observer Service (later to be the Royal Observer Corps). Furnival set up an Operations Room and was able both to co-ordinate the information coming in but also transfer that information the airborne aircraft. Thus they were able to provide information which would best place their fighters to attack the enemy.

Note: references to 'Giant' and 'Giants' which will follow are a generic term often associated with the German heavier than air raiders of WW 1. The principal long range bomber of the Luftstreikräfte (Imperial Air Force) was the Gotha G.V but the Zeppelin-Staaken Riesenflugzeuge (Giant aircraft) was also encountered on the Western Front and crossed the Channel to bomb England. This was shortened to 'Giant' or Gigant' and used to describe the German raiders. Much as in the same way the lighter than air machines were all called Zeppelins although many were built (including the first one to be shot down) by Schutte-Lantz

Pilots and crewmen of No. 141 Squadron at Biggin Hill standing in front of their Bristol F 2b fighters. Note the cock symbol on the side of the aircraft.

(RAF Museum)

June 1918, Capt Baker DSO, acting CO.

During September 1918, the squadron took part in a competition, culminating in a test of flying skills and a Concours d'Elegance at Suttons Farm (Essex) on the 22 September.
One Bristol Fighter, that of Lieut Easall of 'A' Flight, was painted an overall pale blue, while others were painted with stripes. No. 141 Squadron won and were presented with a silver trophy and the title of Cock Squadron. Hence the fighting cocks later painted on the sides of the aircraft. Unfortunately the celebrations were marred when a returning Bristol nose-dived into the aerodrome, killing the crew.

Above: Pilots of No. 141 Squadron celebrate winning the test of flying skills
and a *Concours d'Elegance* at Suttons Farm (Essex), despite the loss of
one of their crews on the return to Biggin Hill. Directly below the cock chicken,
smiling and without flying helmet, is Lt Turner who scored the first 'kill'.
(RAF Museum)

Radio Direction Finding

In April 1918 the RFC and the RNAS had been amalgamated in the Royal
Air Force which had grown during the duration of the war from a support
Corps for the army and Navy to the third independent service. Aircraft too
had developed and destructive potential had been recognised. RAF Biggin
Hill would play a key role in defence of the Realm when was again to come
under attack from the air, but in the meantime it continued to expand as a
seat of experimentation and development. To this end the Wireless Experimental Establishment (WEE) came into being at Biggin Hill in April, 1918,

A nice study of a Bristol Fighter and crew at Biggin Hill in 1918. Note the weight on the end of the wireless aerial hanging below the roundel. Once airborne the observer would reel it out and, hopefully, remember to reel it back in before landing. (RAF Museum)

and grew to a staffing level of about 450.

In October, 1918, as negotiations continued to bring the war to a close via an armistice, another Biggin Hill first was acted out. Much work had been done on Direction Finding in terms of location aircraft emitting a signal allowing the pilot to be given a QDM ('Q' code 'Direction Magnetic') to steer to return to base, but to date nobody had used the reverse process of finding the position of the aircraft via equipment on board. This clearly had significance for navigation above the cloud and set constructed of condensers, coils and valves based on the Bellini-Tosi system was installed in the tail of a Handley-Page 0-400 twin engine bomber.

It was quite a new thing to begin to consider how airmen might find their way accurately in poor visibility and inclement weather. Using radio equipment developed by the Royal Air Force Wireless Experimental Establishment, a number of officer passengers and the crew set off for Paris at 12:00 hrs on Saturday, 19 October, 1918, and were almost immediately lost from view. The navigator set a heading of 123 degrees (m) and speed at 50 knots to cross Marden, Kent, at 12:20 hrs, where they took their first radio fix, picking up signals from the radio stations at Poldhu, in Cornwall, and from Chelmsford in Essex. By observing the bearings and drawing them onto the map; the crossing point corresponded to their position. Flying on they crossed the British coast at Dungeness, passed over the channel and crossed the French coast south of Boulogne at approximately 13:18 hrs. Unable to make any visual landfall the heading was altered to 170 degrees (m) and the aircraft flew on until the radio navigator indicated that they had arrived over Paris. Descending through the cloud they emerged within five minutes of their planned arrival time and within sight of both Le Bourget and the Eiffel Tower, landing at 14:59 hrs.

Flying back on Tuesday, 22 October, they departed at 10:00 hrs and crossed the French coast just north of the Somme Estuary at 11:28 hrs and crossed the British coastline, again in the area of Dungeness, at 11:54 hrs. But rather than set a direct heading for Biggin Hill they extended the test by flying west and by 12:49 hrs they were overhead Brighton. From there a heading of 015 degrees brought them back to Biggin Hill to many congratulations.

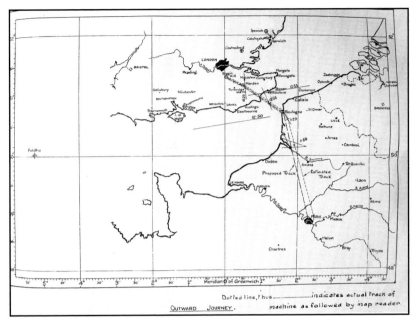

Above: The route out for the RDF trial and, below, the return journey, also by RDF.
(National Archive)

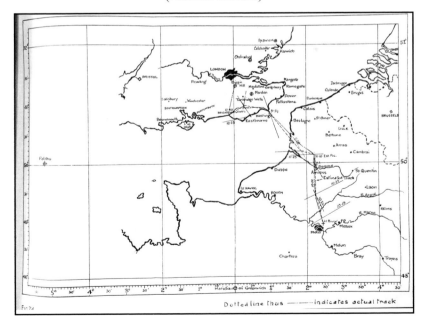

The Handley Page 0-400 preparing for the RDF flight to Paris. Note the crewman in naval uniform who may have been the navigator. (RAF Museum)

Another informative image of the HP 0-400 at Biggin Hill. This is either before or
after the flight to Paris. Note the hangars in the background.
(RAF Museum)

Extract from the Report of the Wireless Experimental Establishment:

The course was altered before Boulogne was approached. Dungeness was passed
about mile away. Brighton was reached exactly on estimated time and the town
passed over.

All calculations in the body of the log, speed, wind, force, and direction etc were
made from wireless fixes with the exception of the first ground speed in each case,
which was found by the ground speed scale of the bearing plates. The only other
instrument available to the navigator was a compass aneroid.

During both flights the navigator had no maps, and was in a position in the back of
the machine near the bomb frames from which it was impossible to check the course
by observation of the ground.

Map Reader's Report.

Without being in touch with the navigator, wireless officer, wireless operator or pilot, the course of the machine over the ground was traced as far as possible.

On the outward journey, visibility over England was poor, but sights taken through gaps in the clouds showed that the machine passed directly over Sevenoaks, Marden and New Romney and was never more than about half to three-quarters of a mile off her course.

Over the Channel visibility through the clouds was almost nil, and it was impossible to trace on the map the course of the machine.

Boulogne was seen for a few seconds, but from there to Paris the visibility was extremely bad and accurate map-reading was impracticable. The weather was unfit for ordinary cross-country flying.

On the return journey on 22 October, visibility was poor to start with, but improved steadily, with occasional bad patches.

The weather was fit but not very favourable for cross-country flying.The track of the machine is shown on copies of charts in Figs. 73 and 74, and is copied from the actual maps (1:250,000) used on the passage.

The trial was therefore an outstanding success and open the way for further developments which were to ultimately result in the blind bombing sets (Oboe) installed towards the later days of WW2. The volume of work carried out at Biggin Hill is also recorded and in the first year from opening as the following extract shows:

Research work during the war was to a considerable extent retarded by the necessity for rapid production of sets for the Services. A considerable amount of research and investigation was, however, carried out, chiefly with regard to valve characteristics, the self-oscillation of valves, and the elimination of magnetic disturbances.

A large amount of inspection was carried out during the year, the following table showing the total number of instruments either 'Passed' or 'Rejected.' Of those rejected, it should be pointed out that some were adjusted subsequently, again tested in the air, and passed fit for service:-

Apparatus	Passed	Rejected
Receivers, Telephone, Wireless, Aircraft, Mark III	737	77
Remote controls for the above	705	35
Receivers, Telephone, Wireless, Aircraft, Mark II	21	1
Remote controls for the above	17	-
Transmitters, Telephone, Wireless, Aircraft, Mark III	443	44
Transmitters, C.W., Type 'W'	13	4
Transmitters, C.W., Mark II	32	27
Capsule Microphones	2967	1050
Generators, DC., H.T., B.H.T. Pattern	326	89
Sets, Field 120-watt Tonic Train (350-360 metres)	1	-
Sets, Field 120-watt Tonic Train (600-1,000 metres)	25	1
Units, H.T., for the above	25	2
Attachments, Telephone, for above	4	-
Receivers, Tf	86	-
Motors, Crypto	3	-
Starters for the above	3	-
Total Tests	**5,480**	**1,330**

The Wireless Experimental Establishment was, therefore, a pretty busy place and with a lot of air testing required, a lot flying was necessary.

Another role for the WEE was to try to establish radio contact with tanks. As with the observation of the fall of shot for the artillery it was important to be able pass accurate battlefield information to the new heavy weapon, the tank. To this end a Mk IV supply tank, No. 402, was pressed into service. The interior of the early tanks was dreadful place to fight with noise and fumes but not entirely unlike the cockpit of an aircraft in flight and presented similar problems in terms of the reliability of radio. No record of how successful these trials were has been found to date by one amusing anecdote has survived. Apparently a small group of young officers decided to take the tank to the mess which was ok in itself but it seems they left the engine running and the beast somehow engaged drive. Thus it was that the steel monster slowly trundled its way across the airfield, through the perimeter fence and across some fields before it could be stopped and recovered.

Two interesting views of the 'Biggin Hill Tank'. Attached to the right side can be seen what seems to be whip aerial. Further to the right, a Bessonneau hangar. Below: the same tank at Biggin Hill with some form of indicator strapped between the tracks.
(Both Tank Museum)

A rather poor but informative image of the 'Biggin Hill Tank' with crew. In the background can be seen the framework of a Bessenneau hangar, either in the process of being erected or dismantled. The ghost of a more substantial building can be seen off to the left. (Karl Middleton)

EARLY DAYS AT BIGGIN HILL

A very mixed group of officers posed in front of a Handley Page 0-400 at Biggin Hill. It is tempting to speculate that this group as a whole was responsible for the successful DF Flight to Paris. Why else would such a group be posing in front of a bomber at Biggin Hill? Below: BE2 of the Wireless Experimental Establishment, Biggin Hill

Often associated with American aircraft of WW2, it is interesting to see the use of 'nose art' on WW1 aircraft. Royal Aircraft Factory BE 2e of the Wireless Experimental Establishment. Below, another example, note the canvass cases covering the propeller blades. Biggin Hill 1918. (RAF Museum)

Above: Another nice example of nose art on a BE 2e of the Wireless Experimental
Establishment (WEE) Biggin Hill. Below: Sopwith Dolphin, also of the (WEE),
Bessonneau hangars in the background (RAF Museum)

Above: Spad VII (A8799) of the WEE, Biggin Hill, more permanent hangars under construction in the background. Below: Sopwith Pup, Sopwith Camel 1F.1 and Sopwith 1½ Strutter standing outside a canvass hangar. Snow covered ground. (RAF Museum)

RFC Motor Transport Section on some form of exercise. Possibly taken in what is now Main Road Biggin Hill. (RAF Museum)

Above: Sopwith 5F.1 Dolphin, front view on the ground with RFC servicemen, standing outside Bessonneau (Type H) hangars. Below: Sopwith Camel following a flying accident, unfortunately all too common in the early days of flying. (RAF Museum)

Two views of a the wreckage of a Bristol F.2b of No.141 Squadron, after being crashed by Captain NH Dimmock, near Downe, 1918. (RAF Museum)

CHAPTER FOUR

AIR DEFENCE EXPERIMENTAL ESTABLISHMENT (ADEE) BIGGIN HILL

The Acoustic Detection of Aircraft

One of the great realisations of the First World War (also known as the Great War) was that the aircraft had developed from a flimsy machine with little potential, other than to take the eyes of the pilot and/or observer to a point where they could gather meaningful information, to a beast of burden with huge destructive potential. It was also clear, from the Zeppelin raids from 1915 onward to the later raids by the first heavier than air machines, that the United Kingdom was now vulnerable to attack from Europe, and possibly on a huge scale.

During the four years of the Great War, as is common in most conflicts, great strides were taken to improve how man could obliterate man more efficiently. It is also often observed that great wars begin with the weapons and tactics of the last major conflict, though not necessarily involving the former combatants. Prior to the Great War the most significant campaign had been the American Civil War, which had ended with trench warfare, static heavy artillery, machine guns and breach-loading rifles, observation balloons, ironclad leviathans of ships and submarines – pretty much how the First World War began. By the end of the 'War To End All Wars' battle fronts had become more fluid, the tank was making an impression and, above all, aircraft and dirigibles had made their destructive debut.

On the night of 19/20 January 1915, the first raid by Zeppelin-type dirigibles crossed the English coast, near the Humber estuary, and turned south. With no great precision, they unloaded their bombs, causing four deaths and sixteen injuries in the towns of Yarmouth, King's Lynn and Sheringham. Although raids continued it wasn't until May that Keiser Wilhelm sanctioned the bombing of London, presumably to avoid the embarrassment of killing or maiming his relatives. On the night of the 31 May, Hauptmann (Captain) Karl Linnarz, an experienced Zeppelin captain, set off on the prevailing winds in LZ 38 and, when over the capital, began releasing his bomb load. Number 16, Alkham Road, Stoke Newington, had the dubious distinction of sustaining London's first bomb damage. The first explosive device to fall on the city proper exploded when it hit the top of a lamppost at the end of Dolphin Passage, Clerkenwell. Further crude incendiaries and explosives totalling more than a tonne were dropped, killing seven, injuring thirty-five and starting numerous fires.

The raids continued for the remaining three years of the war but with escalating losses of airships, the first raids by heavier than air machines began. On 13 June 1917, a force of 14 Gothas bombed London in daylight, killing 162 (including 18 children in a school in Poplar) and injuring over twice as many, returning to base virtually unmolested. It was described as, '… the beginning of a new epoch in the history of warfare.' So serious was the perception of the threat (though, to put things in perspective, a year earlier 56,000 British troops had become casualties on the first day of the Battle of the Somme and 800,000 French and German combatants had perished during the battle of Verdun) that political expediency demanded No. 56 Squadron, RFC, who boasted several aces in their number and a magnificent combat record, should be ordered back to 'Blighty'. On 21 June they arrived and were positioned to wreak havoc on the next Gotha raid (which they undoubtedly would have), with 'B' & 'C' Flights being stationed at Bekesbourne, Kent, and 'A' Flight at Rochford (Southend), Essex. This was, effectively, a very potent vice to be closed on any further bombers following the expected course up the Thames Estuary. With nothing happening for a fortnight, and with pressure for the fighters to be returned to the Front, on the afternoon of the 5 July, the Squadron flew back to Liettres, Nord-Pas-de-Calais; just two days later, on 7 July, 22 Gothas struck again killing 57 and injuring 200.

Public reaction to the raids was swift in coming when anyone or anything with a perceived German connection was beaten, broken or burned. The official reaction was equally expedient; the Prime Minister, David Lloyd-George, appointed the seasoned campaigner,

Lt-General Jan Smuts, to head up a board with the grand title of the Air Organisation and Home Defence Against Air Raids Committee (AOHD-FAARC). This led to the decision in August to put all control of the defending forces (RFC, RNAS, AA Artillery and searchlights) under the single command of Brigadier General Edward 'Splash' Ashmore, a decorated RFC pilot who had gone on to command an artillery division. The new command was to be called the more succinct, London Air Defence Area (LADA) and the quickly devised plan was to have three defensive rings around the capital, the outer ring consisting of anti-aircraft guns and searchlights, the middle ring to be populated with fighters with searchlight assistance and the inner-most ring another concentration of AA guns and lights.

Although the last Gotha raid took place on the night of 19 May, 1918 (during which RAF Biggin Hill was to record its first of some 1400 'kills'), the defence system developed with rudimentary radio contact with airborne fighters and information being fed in from the Metropolitan Observation Service (which was to be consolidated, in 1925, into the Royal Observer Corps) to a central control room, was established near Horse Guards Parade. There, a large map table had been laid out with coloured counters which could be moved about as information on the direction and size of potential raids came in. Information was then relayed out to sub-controls and fighters would be scrambled to intercept, some by now remaining in contact by wireless; very much the model so successfully developed later for the defence of Britain from the Luftwaffe.

However, two major shortcomings hobbled the system - how to detect incoming raiders before they crossed the coast and, once over the UK, how to find them, illuminate them, and shoot them down. The building blocks, although not the final solution, lay again in the First World War, where Lieutenant (later Major) William Sansome Tucker had been part of the research team investigating the acoustic location of enemy guns by the use of crude microphones and trigonometry. He had also proposed that his technique could be applied equally well to the location of aircraft, and as we will see later, he was to be appointed Director of Acoustic Research – Air Defence Experimental Establishment (ADEE) located in War Office site, South Camp at Biggin Hill.

The Germans had raided London and other cities in the Zeppelin airships, Zeppelin-Staaken and Gotha bombers, resulting in 1,400 fatalities and 3,300 wounded. Looking forward, the inter-war theorist, Basil Liddel-Hart, suggested that up to 250,000 people could be killed in London in the first week of an all-out air attack on London; this was enough, just pre-WW2, for the government to have over a million cardboard coffins prepared. In November, 1932, Stanley Baldwin (echoing Giulio Douhet) was to issue his stark warning that,

'The bomber will always get through…'

And Churchill, with his usual chilling eloquence, said about London,

'With our enormous Metropolis here, the greatest target in the world, a kind of tremendous fat cow, a valuable fat cow tied up to attract the beasts of prey…'

Detection was, therefore, the key and here it needs to be emphasised that nothing like RADAR was even a glint in anyone's eye until the mid-nineteen-thirties. So for twenty years the only possibility was the steady improvement of visual observation, aided by searchlights at night, and the development of the new science of acoustics. To underscore this, the first mention I can find in official minutes of RADAR (or RDF as it was first know – Radio Direction Finding) is in those of the first meeting of Sir Henry Tizard's Committee for the Scientific Survey of Air Defence (of which we will hear more later) which met for the first time on Monday, 28 January 1935, at the Air Ministry.

At minute 3.(A) is recorded the following:

d) The possibility of detecting short wave electromagnetic radiation reflected from the metal surfaces of an aircraft, using a ground source, was discussed. D.S.R. (Director of Scientific Research – HE Wimperis) said that Mr. Watson Watt had prepared a memorandum on the uses of short wave electro-magnetic radiation for defence purposes, which would be circulated to the Committee. Mr. Watson Watt considered that there was some hope of detecting by these means. It was decided that further consideration should be given to this possibility after Mr Watson Watt's memorandum has been circulated.

It is also singularly odd to consider that the birth of RADAR grew out of a request to the Radio Research Station of the Department of Industrial Research at Ditton Park, Datchet, Slough, to consider how much power would be needed to produce a death ray that would either stop the engines of aircraft or raise the blood temperature of the crew to fever point. The request from HE Wimperis, the DSR at the Air Ministry (see above) went to the Superintendent of the station, Alexander Watson-Watt. He, in turn, delegated the work to his assistant, Arnold Wilkins, who processed the maths and opined that there simply wasn't enough power available to make such a ray. He did, however, comment on some reflections which had been received from aircraft passing through electromagnetic beams.

On 26 February 1935, Arnold Wilkins set up the Daventry Experiment which first demonstrated that electromagnetic reflections from a Handley Page Heyford could be monitored (for eight miles). Up until that time there was nothing in the offing which could secure better warning of the approach of aircraft, other than the limited vision of the human eye, extended by means of constant standing patrols of aircraft – both consumptive of fuel, wearing on airframes and engines, and fatiguing for aircrew. The science of acoustic detection therefore seemed to offer a solution in the immediate post-war years. It is crucial to understand this and to realise what an important role Biggin Hill played in this (then) cutting edge research at the Air Defence Experimental Establishment in South Camp.

The science of acoustic detection began life as gun sound ranging on the Western Front, and gave birth to the first limb of acoustic research. From quite early on all sides tried to develop some accurate means of using the sound of the discharge of large calibre guns to locate them and, ultimately, call down suppressive fire upon them. Part of this work fell to the Field Survey Battalions who were cartographers and surveyors who, like Marconi's men who had been drawn in to develop wireless, had been seconded to the Royal Engineers for the duration. This was no remote desk job and these erstwhile academics were exposed to considerable danger in their new work.

Simply beginning with the naked human ear, it became clear that if bearings could be taken of the discharge of an artillery piece, at the same time and from different locations, these could be plotted on a battlefield map, and a fair idea of the location of heavy ordinance could be estimated. The first challenge was to improve the sensitivity of the means of location and thus to improve accuracy. To this end Major WL Bragg, an established pre-war scientist, was appointed as an advisor to Sound Ranging at General Head Quarters, France, map section. He was one of the most brilliant minds of the time and was to share a Nobel Prize with his father, WH Bragg, for their services in the analysis of crystal structure by means of x-ray. However his time in France didn't mean he was chained to a desk in the safety of the rear echelon; he was to win the Military Cross and be awarded an OBE for his work.

Bragg and his team had noticed that there were two sounds which accompanied the fall of shot from an artillery piece. First to arrive was the shell and the high frequency sound of its passage through the atmosphere at supersonic speed, a sonic boom. Shortly afterwards came the low frequency boom from the muzzle of the gun, travelling at the speed of sound. A 155mm shell would have a muzzle velocity of around 550 metres/second (depending on the charge and the length of the barrel) and the speed of sound at sea level is in the area of 340 metres/second. It therefore follows that the shell will always arrive before the sound of the gun firing it (unless fired in a high trajectory when it will effectively have further to travel), and it will produce a supersonic sonic pressure wave. This is the rattling crash that arrives with the shell, usually followed by the distant, softer 'boom' of the gun. The distinction between the 'shell wave' and the 'gun wave' was important because of their frequency and power. What was needed was a piece of equipment which was more accurate and precise than the human ear.

This was eventually offered by observations of a mouse hole by Lieutenant William Sansome Tucker who, like Bragg, was another academic drafted into service for the duration. Tucker was either seated in a field toilet or lying on his bunk, the story varies, when he observed a draft of air which accompanied the distant boom of an artillery piece through a mouse or knot hole in the wooden wall. He immediately made the connection that if that draft could be used to cool a heated wire; the resistance would change and could be measured on a galvanometer. Of course the wire didn't have to be stretched across a mouse hole; any open vessel would do and empty stone rum jars were pressed into service. Thus the 'hot wire microphone' came into being and was incorporated in the effort to locate enemy guns.

This developed into a pre-determined string of microphones which would record the muzzle reports of big guns and, through calculations based in the position of the individual microphones and the time delay relative to the others in the system, the position of the gun could be calculated with great accuracy, often bringing swift and accurate retribution on the unfortunate gun crew. This was a science in its own right and was to continue to develop into the system which is still employed today to determine the location and type of heavy weaponry, and even small arms, on the battlefield. It is one limb of the research that was initially conceived on the Western Front, taken up by the Munitions Inventions Department of the United Kingdom Ministry of Munitions and developed; first at Imber Court, Thames Ditton (now a Metropolitan Police Sports and Social Club), then moving to Woolwich, and finally coming to the ADEE at Biggin Hill. However, interest in acoustics had produced the second limb of research which had manifested itself in the form of aircraft detection and was based on 'listening wells'.

A certain Lieutenant Moubray had also been considering the use of acoustics, but in relation to the detection of the height and speed of enemy aircraft. To this end he employed 'listening wells', which were shafts dug to various depths and dimensions, at the bottom of which usually sat an unfortunate squaddie. Also at the bottom of the well was a horn-shaped trumpet which terminated in a stethoscope, to which the aforementioned soldier

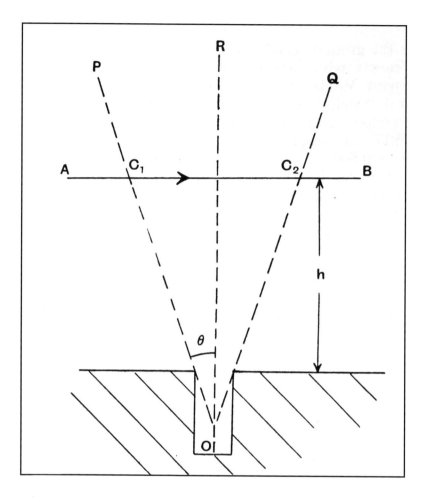

The sound-location unit in the system was a shaft or 'well' sunk in the ground. It was found by experiment that, to an observer situated at the bottom of the well, the sound of the aeroplane passing overhead could be heard only when the machine was within a certain cone with its axis vertical and its apex at the well. In the diagram a well is shown in section, the observer being O. If an aircraft pursues the course indicated be the line AB, the observer first hears the sound when the machine reaches the position C1 where AB cuts OP, and the sound is lost after the aircraft passes C2 where AB cuts OQ. The lines OP and OQ show in section the limits of the cone within which an aircraft must be in order that its sound may be heard by an Observer at O. The vertical line OR is the axis of the cone. It will be convenient to refer to this cone as the 'cone of audibility'.
(Quoted from a War Office paper on acoustics)

would listen intently. With much of the side-line noise around the well reduced, the passing of an aircraft overhead was all the more apparent, even when it could not be seen through fog, smoke or even at night. According to the depth of the well and its width, a 'cone of audibility' was created above the well, increasing in effective diameter as the cone splayed out above the well, usually at about 20 degrees to the vertical. Calculations could be made so that at a given height, say 6,000 feet, the diameter of the cross section of the listening area of the cone could overlap with that of another well, giving constant results as an aircraft passed from the cone of one well to another. This would obviously offer the opportunity to log the speed of the machine as well as its heading. Also, by logging when an aircraft 'cut in' to the cone and when it 'cut out' and, given and estimate of its speed, a slide rule calculation could determine its altitude by the time it took to cross the cone of audibility. The higher up the cone, the wider it became and, consequently, the longer it would take to traverse.

At one and the same time research began in earnest into the defence properties of a third line of acoustic research, 'sound mirrors'. This is defined below as recorded in the publication, 'The Theory of Anti-Aircraft Sound Location and Direction 1932 – War Office'.

> 'The term "sound mirror" is used to describe any instrument which produces intensification of sound by the reflection of the sound waves at a surface and the formation of a focus.'

Sansome Tucker, now promoted to Captain, was seconded to the Munitions Inventions Department (MID) at Imber Court to further investigate the development of listening wells, as well as sound mirrors. We will develop the thread of listening wells and their relationship with yet another development, 'disc systems' with ADEE Biggin Hill a little later, but first we must look at the first appearance of what was to become one of the core research projects. In the early days of the war the French were beginning to experiment with acoustic detection of aircraft and this prompted the Superintendent of the Royal Aircraft Factory, Farnborough, to contact Professor Mather at the City in Guilds Engineering College in South Kensington. He was recommended as someone who seemed to know something about the subject and had conducted small scale experiments in 1915, using what he called a sound reflector. Encouraged by the results a larger, 16 foot diameter (4.8m) reflector, taking the shape of part of a sphere (a spherical segment) and angled up a few degrees above the horizon was cut into a chalk escarpment near Binbury Manor, close to the perimeter of the RNAS Station at Detling, in Kent.

The first sound mirror cut into the chalk at Binbury Manor near Detling airfield. The platform was used by the operator to gather sound though a collector and stethoscope. Note the second figure rather precariously perched at the top right.
(Courtesy of the Royal Artillery Historical Trust)

To provide a more durable surface and to obtain better results the mirror's face was rendered with cement. Mather wrote to the War Office (WO) on 14 September 1915, reporting on his experiments with the larger reflector.

He wrote that they could detect the 70 HP Renault engine of an aircraft at a distance of 10½ miles (16.8km), and could track its progress within 2 or 3 degrees of arc. He went on to say that he had copied the results to the Admiralty because it was the RNAS Station at Eastchurch, Isle of Sheppey, which had provided the aircraft. Primarily, however, he wanted to call the attention of the WO to the results as he believed that over and above the obvious use in aircraft detection, '… such reflectors might be of use in detecting movements going on behind the enemies lines in France and Flanders, more especially after dark.' 'On several nights,' he continued, 'we have heard at Binbury the noise of Railway trains between Southend and Shoeburyness, and also determined the direction of the movement' (Shoeburyness lies on the northern side of the Thames Estuary, about sixteen miles to the north-north-east of Binbury). He also suggested that a portable version of the reflector could be made to put at the disposal of the WO.

Mather and his colleagues filed a more detailed report on further experiments at Binbury Manor which also involved an aircraft from RNAS Station at Eastchurch, flown by Sub Lt Baudry. The reflector was cut into the chalk face to effectively tilt it up at an angle of one in eight, which projected the centre line or focus stretching out to record an aircraft at an altitude of 5,000ft (1524m) at eight miles (12.8km). The focus was 10ft (3m) away from the centre of the reflector, and the 'listener' stood on a wooden platform (see illustration). The approaching aircraft was heard for about three minutes using the reflector, as against only half a minute using the unaided ear. Going away (because the exhausts faced backwards) the aircraft could be heard for five minutes with the ear but for over ten minutes with the reflector, at which time the sound became intermittent. It was later discovered that the cause of the short losses of reception were because the aircraft was climbing in a spiral and only occasionally exposing the rear facing exhaust to the reflector. The altitude of the aircraft when monitored was 4,500ft (1371m) and it had been 10½ miles (16.8km) away.

The conclusion was that larger reflectors might increase the range of audibility and larger targets like Zeppelins with more engines and gearing could possibly heard out to 20 miles (32km) which would be worthwhile. Mather also recommended that such reflectors should be positioned on a flat hill top away from trees or at a reasonable height above the sea at the coast and far enough back to deaden the sound of waves. He also suggested that coastal listening devices could also be used at night to detect submarines running on the surface or any other shipping which could not be accounted for. This work led to the establishment of two new reflectors at Fan Hole north-east of Dover and Joss Gap on the north-east coast of the Isle of Thanet. The Fan Hole site was recently uncovered in an extensive excavation by archaeologists in 2014/15, having been buried in 1975 by Kent County Council, who wanted to tidy up 'unsightly wartime relics', but any trace of the Joss Gap installations have been long lost to coastal erosion. It also appears that Professor Mather, then serving as a Major in the Royal Engineers, was involved in the construction of both mirrors.

One of the two mirrors at Fan Hole near Dover. What the purpose of the walls in front were is unclear, but they were presumably added after the mirrors went out of use. It is at this site that the underground (shelter) tunnels were recently (2015) cleared and opened to the public. Apparently the same digger driver who was tasked with burying them in 1975 was the same contractor who was tasked with uncovering them in 2014.

Above: The second mirror at Fan Hole, slightly tilted backward, presumably to get elevation information. Below: The Fan Hole site on the right showing the position of the mirrors relative to Dover Harbour.

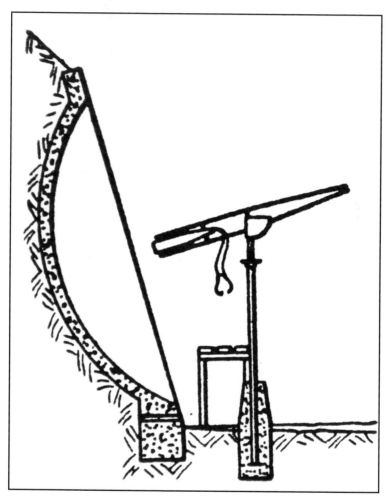

A cross sectional diagram of an early design of sound mirror, such as those first used at Binbury Manor and, later, at Joss Bay and Fan Hole. The first mirror to be built at Hythe was also let into the escarpment, but all subsequent designs were free standing and evolved more into a paraboloid from the segment of a regular sphere shown above.

Joss Bay twin skinned disc. This was to evolve into the horizontal disc that would form
the basis of the Biggin Hill System and later the huge Romney Marsh System.
(Courtesy of the Royal Artillery Historical Trust)

Here we have to realise that there are several threads to this developmental
work and several locations, together with a need to hop back and forth in
time to follow the threads; explore new ones; and move freely from one to
another. The representation of this in a clear narrative and chronological
time line therefore presents something of a challenge, but we will do our
best to describe the evolution of the interwoven disciplines implicit in the
science of acoustics.

Another view of the Joss Bay installation, showing the hutted accommodation on the beach.(Courtesy of the Royal Artillery Historical Trust)

Continuing with sound location, Captain Tucker was very much involved in this line of research and development and recorded that the two new coastal mirrors covered the approaches from Zeebrugger to Calais. He also recorded that the Joss Gap mirror was cut to a radius of 9½ ft (2.8m), was angled up at 15 degrees and was 15ft (4.5m) in diameter. Initially it had a collector trumpet carved from wood which funnelled sound to a stethoscope worn by the operator standing on a platform, but this was later modified to hold a microphone, and for the operator to use headphones. Both mirrors saw active service before air raids ceased and valuable information was sent to the Dover anti-aircraft defences. It was a good foundation on which to build this new form of early warning which would have its roots firmly planted in the War Office site at Biggin Hill.

Whilst the mirror at Fan Hole, as well as that at Joss Gap, continued in their original form providing research information to better improve the fixed mirror, at Joss Gap a newer type was to be trialled. Two flat discs had been assembled with a listening device between them and the whole assembly mounted in the vertical plane on pivots. These two distinctly different types of acoustic detectors continued to produce encouraging results, especially the more versatile disc at Joss Gap, which sat near the chalk reflector cut in the cliff and could be turned to maximise sound reception and indicate the direction of the source. It was, in fact, a development from the listening wells which had, by then, morphed into flat discs. The work on the wells had continued at Imber Court where they were still evaluating and improving them. By beginning to substitute microphones and galvanometers for soldiers, greater accuracy was achieved and it was even speculated that they might eventually be able to differentiate between allied and enemy aircraft.

The horizontal disc had become a spin off from the sound wells. The discs were twenty feet in diameter, their dimensions being determined by the laws of sound physics and wave length. Suffice it to say, it was found that sound was concentrated in the centre of the disc and that a microphone, fitted centrally underneath by way of a hatchway, could register the sound extremely accurately. Later, two disks would be used with a space between them and, by varying the gap the amplification of sound by a factor of 10-20 times could be achieved (see Joss Gap above). The horizontal system still exploited the function of the gap by having the single disc supported on timber supports about eighteen inches above a smooth concrete base. Finally turf was laid across the disc and banked up around it to minimise extraneous noise. This allowed an annular gap around the disc through which sound could penetrate and be received by the microphone in the centre (see illustration).

The discs had been tried at the Signals Experimental Establishment (SEE) which was based in hutted accommodation on Woolwich Common, but it was to fall to the staff of the ADEE at Biggin Hill to expand and develop the theory, the first horizontal disc system being introduced around Biggin Hill and its environs. This was laid out and extended between late 1919 and 1923 and involved up to 12 stations and was entitled, the 'Biggin Hill System'. Stations were built at Downe, Biggin Hill Airfield, Biggin Hill Village, Addington Village, Hesiers Lane, Tatsfield Church, Beddlestead, Luxted, Farley, Titsey, Woldingham and Warlingham. All of the sites were wired into a control room at Biggin Hill, either by GPO lines or lines laid by the Corps of Signals which were, apparently, preferred, being more reliable. This was to be later linked with searchlight stations which were sited as far away as Pains Hill Station (south of Limpsfield), Squerrys Park, (south of Westerham), and Penn Farm, (south of Sundridge). Closer to home, searchlight units may have occupied the same sites as the 20ft (6m) discs being recorded at grid references at Cudham (probably Downe), Beddlestead, Tatsfield, Woldingham, Farley and at Addington.

One of the horizontal discs in the Biggin Hill System. Note the cable leading away from the central microphone. (Courtesy of the Royal Artillery Historical Trust)

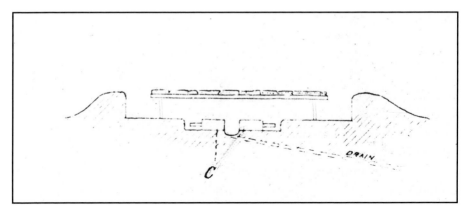

A rather crude drawing of the disc and pit. Covered with turf and with more banked up around it, the microphone was centrally placed.

(Courtesy of the Royal Artillery Historical Trust)

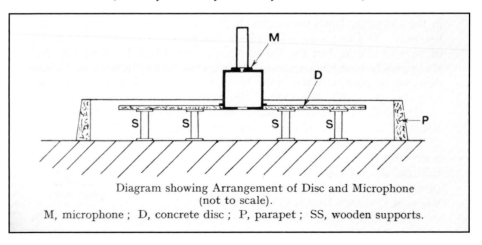

Diagram showing Arrangement of Disc and Microphone
(not to scale).
M, microphone ; D, concrete disc ; P, parapet ; SS, wooden supports.

A later, more sophisticated, horizontal disc which was more like that which was to be developed at Biggin Hill for the huge Romney Marsh System.

(Courtesy of the Royal Artillery Historical Trust)

Therefore gun ranging, the detection of aircraft passing over by means of listening wells, and later discs, and the direct detection of distant targets by means of sound reflectors or sound mirrors, were the three applications of acoustics which had been investigated throughout World War I. Post war it was crystal clear that a means of detection had to be established to defend against the demonstrative power of the newly emerging weapon of warfare – air power. Gun ranging developed into its own special science although most of the early work was undertaken at the ADEE at Biggin Hill. The disc systems were installed and developed and the early sound mirrors tested and modified.

All this research was, by 1919/20, now beginning to become concentrated on the War Office site south of the airfield. It is hard to believe today that this site occupied an area of approximately 26 acres (10.6 hectare), which has now all but disappeared under housing and industrial development; it was once home to a huge concentration of manpower and technical stores. Generally entitled the Air Defence Experimental Establishment (ADEE), it included the RAF Wireless Experimental Establishment (WEE) and the Anti-Aircraft School and was home to in excess of a thousand personnel. In terms of accommodation it had the Officers' Mess for the airfield (Koonowla – also known as the Red House), two other Officers' Messes (presumably one for the Royal Engineers and one for the Royal Artillery), Warrant Officers' accommodation, a Sergeants' Mess, a large Other Ranks Mess, married quarters (of which six remain at the far end of Dowding Close), single officers' quarters and numerous other barrack blocks. On the technical side there were a large number of laboratories, workshops, stores, lecture rooms, a conference room, a large 'B' Type hangar, motor transport sections and innumerable huts and sheds. It was certainly large enough to support its own hospital and mortuary, which were situated towards the eastern side of the site. It also had a large recreation field which was often used for departmental and inter-service sports days, tennis courts and a racquet court (squash) which, at that time, was probably restricted to officers' use. It was a hive of research activity and closely attached to the airfield for the provision of aircraft for experimental purposes and for targets. On this now largely forgotten area were forged the component parts of the system that was to defeat the Luftwaffe in 1940 and beyond.

Key to defence would be acoustic detection, the development of which, remembering that RADAR was still twenty years in the future, gained pace as we enter the early nineteen twenties. The RFC element which had been part of the SEE camp at Woolwich Common moved to the RAF Wireless Experimental Establishment in South Camp and staffed-up to 74 Officers, 35 Warrant Officers, Sergeants and Corporals, 194 Other Ranks, 194 Women and 28 female domestic staff, in all some 525 people. Other key personnel also moved to ADEE Biggin Hill and Dr William Sansome Tucker (who dropped his military title of Major in favour of his pre-war doctorate when he was demobbed) drew together a team to develop all aspects of the new science of acoustics. This, as indicated above, had now precipitated out into three distinct disciplines but which overlapped in many places. Gun ranging was still being refined and has continued in unbroken use by the army to this day. Sound mirrors were to be constructed along the south coast and eventually up the east coast towards the north with research and development still firmly based at Biggin Hill. Lastly, the horizontal disc system, which would track the progress of enemy aircraft, and sound locators, which would guide searchlights and anti-aircraft guns onto their targets at night, would continue to evolve.

To gauge the importance of Biggin Hill in the development of the Defence of the United Kingdom it is worth quoting from a letter to the Air Ministry from the Treasury Chambers:

Sir, In reply to Sir. B.Cubit's letter of the 24th ultimo, 79/1127(M.G.O.F.b) relative to the proposed concentration at Biggin Hill Aerodrome of the various Army and Air Force units concerned in the development of the methods of defence of Great Britain against aerial attack, I am directed by the Lords Commissioners of His Majesty's Treasury to transmit herewith copy of a letter of even date which they have caused to be addressed to the Air Ministry.

My Lords give Their sanction for the necessary expenditure on reconditioning the huts in the southern sector of the aerodrome at an estimated cost of £7,500 on the understanding that the expenditure during this current financial year will be found from savings on Part 1 services.

I am to enquire whether the camp at Perham Down will in consequence of this concentration be thrown up for disposal...

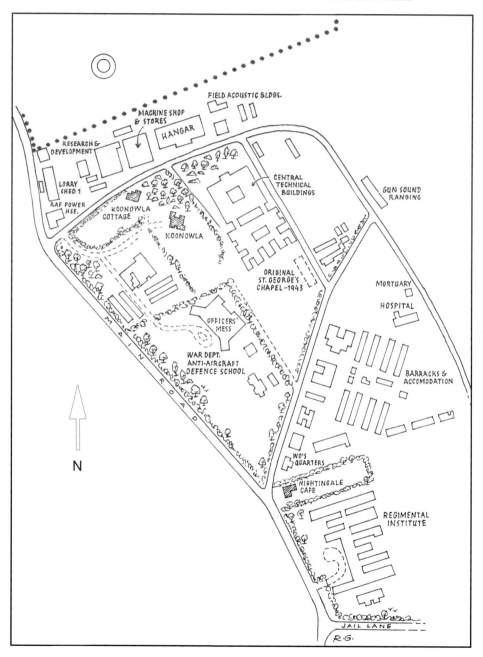

This is a well known picture of the airfield, taken from a German *Lufthansa* aircraft on its way to Croydon. Taken in about 1937/1938 it shows the War Office site in the foreground as it was being redeveloped, but the scale of it relative to the active flying area is clear. Middle left on the airfield is the hangar of the Night Flying Section, who provided aircraft to test the discs and sound mirrors. Below and right of that is Koonowla and the newer Officers' Mess. Further right are some of the technical buildings and further over the entrance road, leading to Main Road. The cross-hatched area shows the area where buildings had stood which became the site of new units before WW2. Extreme right can be seen the three blocks of married quarters which still exist. Bottom right hand corner is the complex which is described as the 'Regimental Institute'. Also see aerial picture taken in 1941, reproduced on P. 341.

Anti-aircraft Defence School (Officers' Mess) Biggin Hill. To the right are Officers' Married Quarters. (Tony Lewis - Biggin Hill Then and Now)

The entrance to the War Office site beside what is now 'Squires' builders' merchants in Biggin Hill. The buildings on the right are mainly Warrent Officers' accommodation.
(Tony Lewis - Biggin Hill Then and Now).
Below: A picture captioned as being 'Routine maintenance in the powerhouse, 1929'.

It was therefore clear that all air defence development was being concentrated at Biggin Hill and the £7,500 sanctioned would adjust to about £380,000 today. No mean sum when money was very tight following WW1.

First let us follow the fortunes of the 'Biggin Hill System', the series of disc detectors which laid out across the Kent countryside and into Surrey. As early as October 1919, plans were being drawn to establish a disc system with Biggin Hill Aerodrome in the middle as detailed above. The first was to be constructed on the airfield and was made of concrete segments, producing a finished disc 20ft (6m) in diameter. At one and the same time, sites were being identified and negotiations with farmers entered into to provide the rest of the system. Only a small area was required but in order to preserve the planned layout as much as possible it was not always easy to site the disc where it would least inconvenience the farmer. Consequently the annual rent of about £1 was sometimes bid up to several times that amount by shrewd land owners. At Biggin Hill a special hut had been set aside (or built new) in which the control equipment would be installed and a new screen that could receive the signals from seven discs was built.

By October 1920, three discs were operational and wired into the control room and preliminary tests took place using a Bristol Fighter but no results have survived. The work moved on to 1921 and was slow to develop, mainly because of a lack of transport and a general lack of enthusiasm to spend money on defence post war. However WS Tucker and his team soldiered on and by April they had an NCO and ten men employed in the section. By August they had extended the system by a further three discs and had fenced them off to prevent further investigation of the strange objects by curious horses and cattle. The extension brought the continental flights from London Croydon Airport into range as they headed south-east towards Beachy Head and the short Channel crossing. Equally, returning passenger aircraft followed a reciprocal course and, unwittingly, provided a healthy supply of targets.

From the experience of the First World War it was clear that early warning and communication were the key elements for effective defence, particularly of London. With the rate of climb of intercepting aircraft being something in the order of 1000-1500 ft/min (304m/min – 557m/min) it could take 15-20 minutes to reach intruders after take-off so early warning was vital if eternal standing patrols were to be avoided. Thus the potential to detect airships and aircraft 20 miles (32km) off the coast, establish a confirmation of their course once over the coast, and a warning of their approach to the outer London defence belt were of great interest to the War Office. Thus the developments at Biggin Hill of the disc system were to be expanded closer to the coast, together with consolidation of the experiments with sound mirrors.

The disc system which was to be installed on Romney Marsh was a logical development of the Biggin Hill System. It consisted of two lines of discs, three miles (4.8km) apart and each disc approximately half a mile (.8km) from its neighbour. The seaward line was about three miles inland and the control room was in a hut near the Church at Newchurch, centrally placed between the lines. By the summer of 1924 the system was operational and trials continued apace. Again those involved with the field work were in direct contact with ADEE at Biggin Hill and modifications and changes to the trials were all ordered from centre. Dedicated GPO (General Post Office) telephone lines had been laid so that information collected on the Marsh could be transferred immediately to Biggin Hill, where the rather grandly named Prediction System Computing Centre was based; then on to Uxbridge where a control room was being worked up. This would, of course, develop in time into the command and control centre so famed for its role in the defence of the realm twenty years on.

The early trials proved the worth of the system as aircraft were regularly tracked at up to 10,000ft (3000m) (and on one occasion 27,000ft (8,229m)), with the estimates of speed and course being more than satisfactory. The system was therefore extended over the winter of 1924 to sixteen discs in each line, thirty-two in all. Most of the trials took place in the evening and at night and three Vickers Vimys were provided by the Night Flying Flight, itself based at Biggin Hill, but positioned at Lympne for the trials. In 1924 some 60 crossings of the system were made and during the next year this rose to over 140. Experimentation continued through the early and mid-nineteen-twenties and a wealth of information gathered, but by then the disc

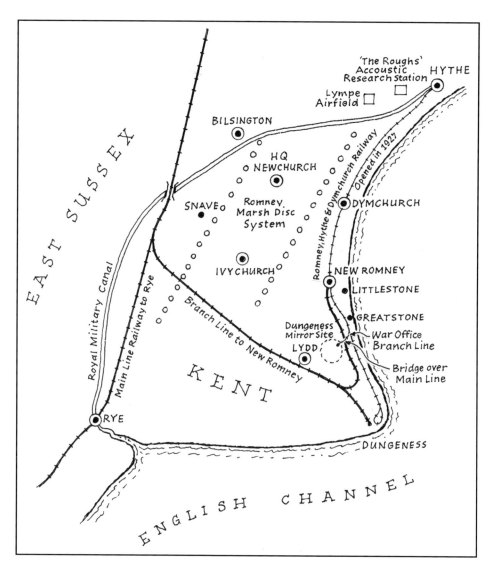

The Romney Marsh System, which was a logical extension of that extensively tested at Biggin Hill. Later, the 'War Office Branch Line' of the RH & D Light Railway carried much of the raw materials to build the mirrors and acoustic wall at Dungeness and, later, transported staff and visiting dignitaries to the site. Although the branch line was lifted the bridge over it for the also now redundant line to New Romney still exists.

(see Appendix - Present Day)

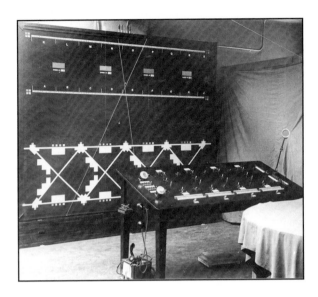

Two views of what is thought to be the control board for the
Romney Marsh System at the Operations Room, Biggin Hill.
(Courtesy of the Royal Artillery Historical Trust)

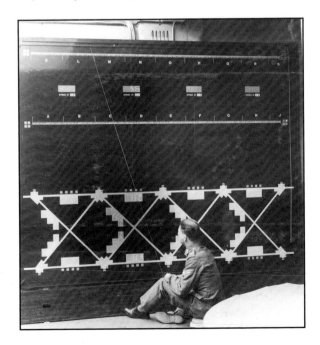

A 32-Line Disc System Indicator.

A 32 line Disc Indicator which was installed in the System HQ at Newchurch.
In front of it can be seen a map of the Marsh, presumably to identify which
discs in the system were registering a contact.
(Courtesy of the Royal Artillery Historical Trust)

system was being eclipsed by the continued development of sound mirrors.
Of this genus there would be the construction of more, particularly along
the south-east coast from Dover to Dungeness. The conclusion had been
reached that the principal use of the disc system was as a silent sentry, but
it was also an economical use of manpower as just two operators could control the full ten miles of its reach.

By the beginning of the early nineteen-twenties, on an area known as the
'Roughs' on the high ground above the Army School of Musketry at Hythe,
a new mirror and a control room were built, entitled the Acoustic Research
Station; it would become the focus for mirror research. But first we have to
return to an earlier time and the disc and mirror at Joss Gap. It was realised
that the nature of the hemispherical reflector was that it concentrated col-

lected sound (or if it had silvered surface it would concentrate light) at a point along centre line called the focus. Conversely, if a source of sound was released at the same point it would be projected out as a beam. This is easiest imagined by using the example of a car headlight or spotlight. The bulb sits at the focus of the silvered reflector and when energised it produces light which is focused and projected as a beam of light. If the position of the bulb is variable along the central axis it is easy to widen or narrow down the beam by moving the bulb in and out. The same physics applies to sound and a sound source placed at the focus will project a beam of sound out, and movement in and out of the source will affect the width of the beam at varying distances from the reflector. This was to be the next limb of the work undertaken at Joss Gap where the reception of sound through the sound mirror was reversed to achieve highly directional transmission of sound.

There seemed to be three likely applications of this emerging technology; medium distance signalling (if wireless was inoperative or jammed), as a navigational aid to shipping, and a similar aid to aircraft. The signalling aspect may or may not have been pursued; examination of the files available only make the odd mention of it and although it seems a likely use of the system it would, of course, be easily open to interception. As a navigational aid to shipping perhaps it makes more sense because the fog horns on the light houses and light ships are generally used to give a broad general warning of danger, of an area to be avoided. However, if it was desired to transmit a homing line for a ship in fog, for instance to navigate towards a harbour mouth or estuary, it seems entirely logical that such a beam could help. Again it's probably worth remembering that at this time there is no land based RADAR to inform ships of their location and heading, or ship-borne RADAR to 'see' through fog and heavy weather and certainly no GPS to locate them within a metre or so.

So how is this tied in with aviation and the ADEE at Biggin Hill? The third application could be the projection of a sound beam, out in marginal conditions, down which a pilot, by idling his engine, could locate himself in the beam and thus make a guided descent through the clag. Very much like a modern instrument landing approach but before such radio beams were available. Thus there is a record of a visit to the Joss Bay site, in June 1920, by a person indicated as the Commandant of Biggin Hill Aerodrome, accompanied by Dr Robinson and Major Erskine-Murray. The Commandant could have been one of two people because at the time there was the Officer Commanding (OC) the RAF Wireless Experimental Establishment, Wing Commander GP Grenfell DSO and the OC RAF Biggin Hill. It is not clear which actually attended but either would arguably be looking for the flying application. Major Erskine-Murray was very much involved with the development of wireless and two years later was to present his paper, Wireless in the Royal Air Force, to the wireless section of the Institution of Electrical Engineers. Secondly, the illustration, showing the huge klaxon at Biggin

An interesting view of what is obviously a huge klaxon or fog horn from a lighthouse on location at Biggin Hill. The hangar in the background is that of the Night Flying Flight standing parallel to Main Road. On the original image, but probably a victim of reproduction, is a faint image through the ground mist - over the top right of the horn - of the Saltbox (see more later) on the western perimeter of the aerodrome.
(Courtesy of the Royal Artillery Historical Trust)

Hill, demonstrates there was some kind of link as the sound generator matches the description which appears in one of the files. Thus it was either the one used at Joss Bay or another being used on parallel research at Biggin Hill. This arm of research was to continue at Biggin Hill as will be described later.

But before we proceed with the story of the mirrors, it is worth consulting an SEE report from June 1925 which refers to the research programme of the previous year and gives a flavour of the early stages of serious research and the difficulties of practical tests. From what is termed the 'First Period' there is a record of the Summer Programme 1924 (5 Aug–29 Sept), part of which is transcribed here. However, it is fair comment that unless the reader is intensely interested in the detail and the feel of the time, little would be lost by jumping to the analysis of the report which follows it.

First Period - During this period the programme originally arranged consisted in flights by Vickers Vimy machines provided by the Night Flying Flight RAF (Fl./Lt. R.Halley DFC, AFC, RAF which was during the period in question stationed at Lympne Kent. The aeroplanes were to leave Lympne and fly out to sea beyond range of the acoustical station at Hythe and then return via at the Disc System which lies between Dymchurch and New Romney (Headquarters Newchurch) and thence over the Prediction System to Biggin Hill. The original plan provided for two aeroplanes every evening at an interval of about half an hour. The data as to early warning obtained from the Acoustical Mirror at Hythe and as to times of crossing the Disc System together with height, speed and course deduced therefrom were collated at Hythe and despatched thence by telephone to Biggin Hill where the Prediction System Computing Centre was situated. This arrangement closely resembled that which would obtain in actual warfare except that the Prediction System was too near the threatened area (viz London). Arrangements were also made for the verification of any predictions given. This was done by providing four searchlight stations which were to open at the predicted time so that their beams would intersect at the Predicted point. Obviously if the prediction had been correct, the target would have been illuminated. It should be noted that the employment of searchlights in this connection was solely for the purpose of checking the results of the Prediction System and was not intended in any way to influence a tactical question of whether they should or should not be used for like purposes in actual warfare. Each of these searchlights had a crew of one NCO and the two men to act as lorry driver and lamp hand respectively. The NCO was responsible for setting the projector to the correct elevation and azimuth and for exposing the beam at the correct moment and was in telephonic communication for these purposes with the Control Position, to which in its turn were transmitted from the Computing Centre, the position of the Predicted Point and the Time Signal. This Control Position was equipped with charts to enable the Predicted Points to be interpreted in terms of angles of elevation and azimuth for each searchlight position and with a stop-watch, which was started at the Signal Time and at the reading of which of 1 minute the order to expose the beams was given. The troops for manning the searchlights and the sound locators together with telephonist for the computing centre was supplied from the 1st Air Defence Brigade, Blackdown and on their arrival had to be trained for the various functions. It was the original intention to give the listeners some training on the Biggin Hill Aerodrome itself before they were sent out to work at the out-stations but unfortunately this proved impossible owing to the extremely short time available between the delivery of the trumpets and the date (Aug 5th) previously fixed for the commencement of the experiments. Thus the listeners had to start straight away on the actual experiments without any previous experience of practice in work entirely new to them and this fact was doubtless all important in accounting for the extremely bad readings obtained during the first period of the work. Whenever possible, practice flights by personnel of 56 (Fighter) Squadron RAF Biggin Hill were carried out to supplement the routine at night flights but this could only be done very seldom since the time taken for the men to get out to the sound locator positions and return and the late hours of the ordinary flight rendered it impractical for them to be sent out more than once a day except on special occasions.

Severe difficulties were also experienced in satisfactorily adapting the searchlight for the special purpose required of them.These appliances were unfortunately all different in pattern and in any case are not designed to be capable of accurate levelling or orientation so that a considerable amount of work had to be done in fitting each with elevation and azimuth scales and even when this had been accomplished it was not found possible to orient the scales correctly owing to the absence of sights or similar devices for the purpose. Finally this orientation was carried out by looking along the sides of the projector barrels and moving them until the line of sight intersected some distant object previously selected by a prismatic compass - a method scarcely productive of very great confidence in the accuracy of the results.

Further, even if the barrel of the project were in the correct position there was no guarantee that the beam would also be projected in the required direction and consequently the orientation was constantly checked either by forming on the crater of the positive carbon an image of the sun at noon or preferably by pointing the beam at the North Star, the elevations of these stars being obtained from a nautical Almanack. By means of these expedients a fair degree of accuracy was obtained and the searchlights when exposed on appropriate angles of azimuth and elevation did provide, in general, a definite into section.

All this work together with instruction of the men (a by lecture) in their various duties had to be carried out between the time of their arrival at Biggin Hill in early July and August 5th, but before this a considerable amount of preparation had to be put in hand. Thus in addition to the design and manufacture of the various instruments required at the Sound Locator Stations and in the Control Centre, sites for the former and for the searchlight stations had to be selected and surveyed and lines laid to them. It has already been stated that the trumpet station lines were provided by the Post Office but those to the searchlights were laid by the Royal Corps of Signals, personnel of the Field Acoustic Section. These latter lines gave little trouble and were seldom out of action.

The site selected for the searchlights were those of the Downe, Biggin, Cudham, Bedlestead, and Tatsfield positions of the School of Anti-Aircraft Defence (SAAD - Biggin Hill), the first named being an alternative position which was not in fact made use of, and these sites were surveyed by the Ordnance Survey Office, Southampton. Their coordinates as well as those of the Woldingham, Farleigh and Addington positions of the SAAD are given for future reference (recorded in the report as grid references).

In analysis, the report reflects that the Romney Marsh disc system was being tested for its capacity to provide information on which a prediction of course, speed, altitude and estimated time of arrival of a target aircraft at a predetermined point could be based. Information was collected from the disc system at the Newchurch HQ hut and passed to Hythe, where readings from the mirror were attached, and then the package passed by telephone to the Prediction System Computing Centre, situated ADEE Biggin Hill. In turn, a position for the target was predicted at a certain time and the information passed by landline to the searchlight projectors who, when ordered, would illuminate a position in the sky. In the event the prediction had been perfect, and the course followed accurately, the target would have been 'coned' by the searchlights. However that was not the purpose of the exercise; it was primarily to establish how accurate a prediction could be produced.

Added to this is comment on the rushed nature of the bringing of new personnel to the project and the poor state of the equipment, for instance the non-standard searchlights which, at that stage, had no means of being laid onto a target. Development of the disc predictor continued but the more sophisticated sound mirrors and sound locators were beginning to render that limb of the research redundant.

Moving forward in time and picking up the thread of the mirrors, it is clear the writing was on the wall for the Romney Marsh disc system; with the success of the mirrors the equipment seemed to have outlived its usefulness. Certainly any plans to expand the system as a primary early warning system along the south and east coast were abandoned, but it still had one more roll of the dice. Towards the end of 1928 and into 1929 the system was used to research the passage of sound waves through changes in atmospherics; but by the beginning of the thirties little more work was done and the wiring and electrical equipment was removed, the fences taken down, most of the discs broken up and the pits infilled over the course of two years. The leases for the sites and access agreements were terminated with the land owners during the financial year 1933/34 and thus ended this limb of the development of acoustical research, but others were still able to stand their ground.

Sandbags and ballast on the Dungeness peninsular heaped up against what must have been one of the last disc sound locators in one of the two lines which stretched from Burmarsh in the north-east of Romney Marsh down onto Dungeness.
Mr Handford is pictured to the left.
(Courtesy of the Royal Artillery Historical Trust)

Mr Handford again, this time standing in the concrete pit which formedthe shell of the disc. The 'lid' was supported by internal posts and the microphone was centrally placed. Sound entered through the annular gap left around the edge of the device. The unmistakable undulating shingle beds of Dungeness stretches out behind.
(Courtesy of the Royal Artillery Historical Trust)

Again Mr Handford is pictured, this time outside the sandbag wall. Clearly looking in the opposite direction as the first picture but again unmistakably Dungeness. Below: A finished disc with microphone installed to record from under the disc. This may be in situ in the system or an experimental model at ADEE Biggin Hill; one is recorded as being located on the aerodrome. (Courtesy of the Royal Artillery Historical Trust)

CHAPTER FIVE

MIRROR, MIRROR AND THE WALL

The Development of the Acoustic Mirror

Moving into the nineteen-twenties, the new ADEE Research Station at Hythe was reaching completion by the end of 1922, and consisted of hutted accommodation for laboratory work and also some accommodation for a resident member of the team. Mr Player had been a Regimental Sergeant Major in the Royal Engineers and had been very much involved in developments at Joss Bay, especially in the sound projection experiments where he took trips on the steamer Royal Sovereign to report on the sound beam; he also spent at least one week on the same observations on the North Foreland light ship. Now out of the army he was very much part of the research furniture and took up residence with his family at the Roughs. In the New Year one of Tucker's colleagues from the First War, Percy Rothwell, who had first-hand battlefield experience of acoustic gun ranging, joined the team and became responsible for the work at Hythe.

As the focus on practical field research of the properties and potential of sound mirrors moved to Hythe, the process of developmental work on acoustics became concentrated at ADEE Biggin Hill. However, the links with SEE at Woolwich Common would remain, as would the association the Royal Ordnance Factory (Woolwich Arsenal) where equipment for sound locators was either built, assembled, or tested before making the short journey to Biggin Hill (but more of that in the next chapter). The first mirror at Hythe differed from those at Binbury Manor and Joss Gap and, to a certain extent, that at Fan Hole, because it was a concrete unit cast on site (as opposed to a semi-sphere carved from a chalk face and rendered with cement). In front of the 20ft (6m) mirror was a concrete pillar on which was mounted a tubular steel arm which could be swung around within the focus of the mirror and give a wide range of monitoring across the Channel. This was fitted with a sound receiving horn tubed to stethoscope type head sets, and also had facilities for microphones. This was still an early design which required an operator to stand on a platform in the open to swing the sound boom. Early tests echoed the work already done, verifying that reception of sound was increased by a factor of about ten over the human ear.

The choice to move from Joss Gap had been motivated, in part, by the relative lack of aeroplane traffic in that area. However, just over a mile to the west-north-west of the Roughs at Hythe, lay Lympne airfield. It was opened in 1916 and by the 1920s was a base for mail carrying aircraft and some early passenger flights, a target rich environment. Neither was it new to acoustic research as aircraft from Biggin Hill had, from time, positioned at Lympne for the tests of the Romney Marsh disc system. Other aircraft on commercial routes across the Channel used Lympne as a turning point to pick up their heading to France (and return) and similar aircraft types, flying to a schedule, were helpful to scientific study.

Research continued and with encouraging results the system was to be expanded. In 1925 Dr Tucker was appointed as the 'Director of Acoustic Research' at ADEE Biggin Hill which gave him overall charge of the main threads of the expanding work. Other mirrors were now in the offing and one was built at Abbot's Cliff, between Folkestone and Dover, and another near New Romney at Greatstone. The latter of the two was the first of what was to become a small concentration of mirrors on the shingle peninsular to the east of Lydd Airport in the area generally referred to as Dungeness; both were scheduled to be completed by March 1928. Official discussion was already of the perceived need to construct a chain of similar mirrors along the length of the south, south-east and east coast, possibly as far north as the Humber River.

The 20 ft mirror at Abbot's Cliff, between Dover and Folkestone, which still exists. The operator was out in the open, with sound being concentrated along the focus of the mirror, then funnelled into the horn-shaped collector and down specially constructed tubes to ear pieces. This was the design first used at Hythe and which became the model be built along the Kent coast. The original at Hythe mirror fell forwards following a land slip in the late 1970s. (Courtesy of the Royal Artillery Historical Trust)

Above: Abbot's Cliff looking north-east.
Below: Looking towards Dover.
(Courtesy of the Royal Artillery Historical Trust)

Although it only took about four weeks to build the foundations and erect the concrete mirror at Hythe, much time was consumed in constructing the access to the sites, laying foundations and assembling hutted accommodation and installing equipment. Thus it was that the March date was soon overrun and concern was being expressed as to whether the 1928 test season (summer) would pass without substantial progress in the research. Hythe became the centre for the construction of the new mirrors and much of the raw materials were delivered there for onward transmission to the other two sites. Abbot's Cliff seemed to progress relatively easily but unforeseen problems dogged the construction at Dungeness, not least of which was the progress of the Romney Hythe and Dymchurch Railway (RH&D), which was apparently inching its way towards its designated terminus at Dungeness lighthouse

The miniature railway was built during the 1920s and opened on 16 July 1927. It had been the dream of millionaire racing drivers Count Louis Zborowski and Captain JEP Howey to develop such a run of miniature track. Louis Zborowski had constructed a railway at Higham Park, his home at Bridge, Kent, and had ordered two small-scale Pacific Class locos of 15" gauge, together with rolling stock. He was however killed in a motor racing accident at Monza before the Romney Marsh site was chosen, and it was therefore left to Howey to take delivery of the new locos and continue the project alone.

With the railway already open and in regular use as far as Hythe, the concern for Tucker and his team was that an extension to Dungeness lighthouse would pass in front of the proposed site, a third of a mile (600m) to the east, and might interfere with readings. The reports refer to the 'approaching construction' of the railway which was, in the end, to have distinct benefits for the sound mirror project. Unlike the fanfare associated with the opening of the first part of the railway, the extension seems just to have quietly become active over the August Bank Holiday of 1928. As far as noise generation was concerned the ADEE team took the view that it wasn't going to be significant, perhaps because the major part of the testing was undertaken in the late evening and during the night when the train wouldn't be running.

The 20 ft mirror, the first to be built on the Dungeness site. It is free standing like the slab models but is of a deeper paraboloid design. However the operator is still required to be outside at the mercy of the elements and sound collecting is still via a collecting horn, tubes and head set.(Courtesy of the Royal Artillery Historical Trust)

The second and larger design to arrive at Dungeness, the 30 ft (9 metre) bowl, angled
back for better collecting of airborne noise and to eliminate, as much as possible,
background interference. The sound collection is still by the collecting horn but
the arm is operated from within the glazed control room and sound piped down
to the seated operator. Standing in front is Percy Rothwell.
(Courtesy of the Royal Artillery Historical Trust)

Above: Another view of the 30 ft mirror showing the series of flat surfaces at the back which were shuttered to form the outer shell. Below: The close proximity of the two mirrors at Dungeness can be appreciated here, as can the progress from the flatter first design to the deeper paraboloid which followed.
(Courtesy of the Royal Artillery Historical Trust)

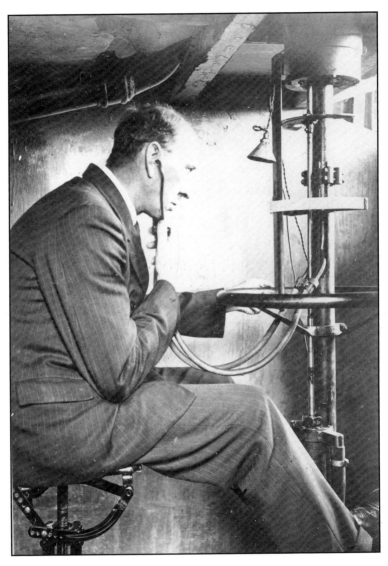

An excellent study of an operator (captioned as Mr Handford in the original file but possibly Dr Paris) in the control room under the 30 ft mirror at Dungeness. The hand wheel moved the sound collector in azimuth (left to right) and foot pedals were used to elevate or depress the position of the collector. The drain pipe above his head and the remains of the operating mechanism make an interesting comparison in the Present Day Appendix. (Courtesy of the Royal Artillery Historical Trust)

The finer design of the Hythe 30 ft bowl (still existing but in a poor state of repair see: Appendix: Present Day) which was altogether more aesthetic. The control room was below it and fully glazed. The sound was collected in the conventional manner, then piped down to the operator below in the Control Room. This followed a more conventional solid 20 ft mirror like that at Abbot's Cliff which was used in conjuction with this newer design. (Courtesy of the Royal Artillery Historical Trust)

Tucker was very heavily involved in the new work and his contact number was given in correspondence as that of the Hythe Station at the Roughs. However his presence was required elsewhere on 28 June when he reported to Buckingham Palace for his award of the OBE by the King.

Moving momentarily back in time to follow the fortunes of the sound mirrors, research at ADEE Biggin Hill and field trials at Abbot's Cliff, Hythe and Dungeness indicated modification to the shape of the sound mirror to be more of a bowl, closer to a parabola than a hemisphere. The logic behind this, I would speculate, was to better concentrate the incoming sound and give a more directional result. A comparison of the shape of the new mirrors and those of the multi-bowl sound locators (which followed) show a continuity of thought. New mirrors were therefore scheduled for Hythe and Dungeness which would not only be of the new deep shape, but also increased in size to 30ft (9m) diameter. That proposed for Dungeness was to be an amalgam of the now traditional slab design and that of the Hythe bowl, and more robust in construction. Hythe was of a new and much finer design, consisting of a metal framework which then bore a steel mesh. This in turn was rendered with cement to give a rather aesthetic result. In form it was much like the RADAR dishes that were to follow within a decade, and which were to be its nemesis.

Remaining within the envelope of the development of acoustics, the construction of the Hythe mirror was completed in the autumn of 1929 and that at Dungeness by the spring of 1930. Working both mirrors together, Tucker and his colleagues were sure they would make a significant step forward and possibly open the door to more sites being commission on the way to a defensive chain along the coast. Indeed, the possibility of units be erected on the Isle of Wight to help protect Portsmouth were already being mooted in command circles.

Another step forward was in a design which brought the operators indoors for the first time. Beneath both the new Hythe and the Dungeness mirrors was a control room from which the sound receiver could be moved around inside the curve of the mirror. Mostly still controlled by the use of tubing and stethoscopes, it was still dependent upon the hearing and skill of the individual to extract the maximum range and accuracy. But electronic means were to be used extensively in the next evolution, the 200ft (61m) wall.

This was also to be sited at Dungeness and would stand beside the 20 & 30ft mirrors already in use. Information and results would also be fed back through the Acoustic Research Station at Hythe for onward transmission to the Acoustic Research Section at ADEE Biggin Hill. The reason for this radical diversion in design was simply that of acoustic wave lengths. The mirrors best operated in the range of relatively short wave length, about

2 - 3ft (.5 - 1m), but some of the lower tones which emanated from slow revving aero engines were in the longer wave ranges of 14 - 18 feet (4 – 5m), some of which would be inaudible to the unassisted ear. This required an increase of the mirror surface by a factor of about ten and it was demonstrably impractical to attempt the construction of a 200ft diameter mirror. The solution was a 200ft curving wall or strip mirror, which would at least take slices of the tones required. The longer wave lengths would travel further (similar to radio waves) than their busy shortwave counterparts and thus increase the range at which their source could be detected.

Whilst an advance in the potential range of the acoustic system, it was also something of a step back as there would be no swinging arm and sound collector but, at least initially, there would be a predetermined path in a 'listening trench' some 75ft (23m) out from the surface of the mirror and about a 100ft (30m) long where listeners would patrol on foot. A more or less permanent fixture at both Dungeness and Hythe was Percy Rothwell, one of Tucker's right hand men from Biggin Hill; also regularly to be seen at both sites was the Director himself.

Approval for the construction of the wall was ratified in the autumn of 1928 and construction began early in 1929. Unusual at the time was the method of construction, if very familiar these days, with more and more reliance on reinforced concrete to form the core of structures. The methodology was familiar for the Royal Engineers, who over saw the projects, because the design and construction of blockhouse defences and pill boxes was part of their stock-in-trade. Timber shuttering and scaffold was erected by contractors around steel reinforcing bars and the concrete poured in sections. The surface of the mirror was to be vertical with the forecourt sloping away to ensure drainage. The rear of the wall was substantially buttressed to offer support against the winter winds which howl in from the Channel from time to time.

Now important to the work at Dungeness, rather than a detractor, was the narrow gauge Romney, Hythe and Dymchurch railway which had, for a short time, caused concern, it now became an important part of the construction. It was agreed that a spur line could be laid so that materials could be loaded into goods waggons (at Hythe and/or New Romney) and hauled to the site by a petrol driven narrow gauge loco. Given that such railways had become quite a feature of the logistics of WW1, it must have been a natural progression for the Royal Engineers to employ such a feature. The gauge of the RH&D, at 15 inches, would have differed from the wartime standard, and the RH&D must have supplied rolling stock from their own inventory, but in essence there was a familiarity for the engineers. Further, a two road wooden shed was erected by the turntable at Hythe and leased to the War Office for the 1929 season. The work for the WO appears to have been done mainly at night and its volume is reflected in the rise of goods transported in 1929. Records show that in 1928, 312 tons (283 tonnes) was carried but in 1929 this rose sharply to 891 tons (808 tonnes). Unfortunately no record survives for 1930, but by 1931 it had returned to a more average and sedate 314 tons (285 tonnes), by which time the bulk of the construction at Dungeness was complete. Staff also travelled as passengers from Hythe and New Romney to the site as the access over the poor roads and strips of shingle was generally poor. The spur line is generally recorded as the War Department Branch and is referred to in several reports and communications between the Officer in Charge, Acoustic Section, Air Defence Experimental Establishment, Hythe, and the Traffic Manager, Mr R Hardie. The arrangement for the use of the railway and the extension were subject to contract, one stipulation being that at the cessation of works the spur line had to be dismantled. In the event, the War Department Branch remained in use for a considerable time beyond that first envisaged. Today the course of the spur line can still be seen, together with a small bridge which carried a footpath over the line.

This wasn't the last military use of the little railway; during WW 2 an armoured train patrolled the line and it was also pressed into service to deliver equipment and accessories to PLUTO (Pipe Line Under the Ocean), the 6" pipe through which fuel was pumped to the advancing Allied armies after D-Day.

Construction of the wall by Messrs Concrete Structures Ltd continued under the supervision of the Royal Engineers (RE) but inevitably overran. The wall itself was completed more or less on schedule, but the forecourt and in particular the listening trench was delaying the completion, commis-

An aerial image of the 200 ft wall soon after construction. The War Office spur line can be seen leading away east to the main RH & D line. (S. McMurray)
Below: The newly completed wall with wind shields deployed at each end and railway line in the foreground. (Courtesy of the Royal Artillery Historical Trust)

The 200 ft wall from the rear. The fine buttressing can be observed as well as the Operations Room and Store which was constructed on the back, complete with chimney. It is interesting to compare how it has weathered in the Appendix: Present Day. Below: The forecourt with the smudge-pot type microphone housings in position. One of the wind breaks can be seen to the left and a scale, presumably bearings, are displayed on a strip along the wall. Mr Handford appears again in the middle left of the picture, apparently inspecting the line of the microphones.(Courtesy of the Royal Artillery Historical Trust)

A view of the Control Room with switches to energise the individual microphones on the forecourt below and galvanometers on the wall to indicate signal strength. The glazed window was a later addition necessitating a hole being cut in the mirror.
(Courtesy of the Royal Artillery Historical Trust)

sioning, and use of the wall. On record are several exchanges between Lt Col. Pemberton of the RE and Major Inglis who was Superintendent of the ADEE, Biggin Hill where the delays can be observed. Fortunately the exchanges seem to have precipitated a ratcheting up in work tempo and the wall was ready by the end of July, 1930. Unlike the dish mirrors, the wall managed two different types of listening work. Sound emissions from potential targets were heard by patrolling sentries who walked their short beats in special rubber-soled shoes and, at one and the same time, by electronic means. This relied, once again, on Tucker's hot wire microphones, 20 of which sat in an arc along the forecourt, each covering 5 degrees of the whole arc of the wall. Each sat like an independent tar pot containing the micro-

Another view of the Control Room at the rear of the 200 ft mirror. Unfortunately the back lighting through the window on what seems to be a very bright day has resulted in this rather dark image. But, nonetheless, the operator can be seen at work.
(Courtesy of the Royal Artillery Historical Trust)

phone and resonator, wired to a board inside the control hut.

After a series of tests, Tucker was able to announce that in ideal conditions the electronic side of detection had successfully tracked an aircraft at a range of 27 miles (43km) and an average range in different conditions of 17-18 miles (30km). This was useful distance, even given that it was realised that since the end of the War the speed of aircraft had increased by a substantial margin.

The last major modification the wall was made in the autumn of 1933 when a hole was cut in it, centrally and about at half height, and a plate of glass set into it. Behind it was built a two storey building which had stores on the ground floor and the control room on the first floor. From the new position the controller had a clear view of the whole forecourt, as well as a clear aspect of the Channel. The wall and the 30 ft mirrors were beginning to provide the hoped for early warning and plans were being made to acquire the required number of sites along the coast to expand the chain. However, within two years the innocuous enquiry from HE Wimperis, Director of Scientific Research, to Alexander Watson Watt, would begin the slow decline in acoustic research at the coastal sites but a different limb of acoustics was still to continue to be developed to good use.

CHAPTER SIX

SOUND LOCATORS AND SEARCHLIGHTS

Guiding Searchlights in the darkness with Sound Locators

The last limb in the field of acoustics to find its home at Biggin Hill, and which will probably have the longest legacy, was that of sound locators. They were very similar in many respects to the large sound mirrors, but with a more immediate purpose and shorter range. Like the sound mirrors and disc systems, the design, research and development was firmly lodged at ADEE, Biggin Hill, within the perimeter on the War Office site in South Camp, as many of the pictures used in this chapter will verify.

Sound locators were based on the simple ability of humans and most animals to be able to tell from which direction a sound is coming. This is achieved instinctively by the brain registering the difference in volume in each ear and turning the head until they are equal. Thus the first 'improvements' on nature involved both channelling more sound to each ear by means of crude amplification (horns), and by effectively further separating the ears by extending the distance between them. On average the ears are about 9 inches (22cm) apart, and the more that gap can effectively be increased, the more accurate the directional estimate – essentially the same as optical range finders. Crude but effective, this led to some spectacular devices which were in sore need of the application of science to refine them.

As described in the previous chapters, it had been realised that to detect the heading and altitude of a source of sound, the two inputs provided by nature (ears) weren't necessarily that efficient and amplification, either through a parabolic reflector or a hemispherical mirror, could be utilised to greatly improve detection. As touched on earlier, a parabolic reflector is shaped so that light or sound entering it, when it is pointing directly at the source, will be concentrated in one point on the centre line, the 'focus'. Therefore, if a microphone or a tube leading to a stethoscope is placed at the point of concentration of the parabola, it will collect the concentrated sound and, by turning the parabola, the source can be targeted and tracked; a quite natural extension of nature. Using a hemispherical fixed mirror (such as those at Hythe and Dungeness) a microphone or a sound collector was moved about on an arm to gain the best return, with the position of it being registered by the free end of the arm and the mirror remaining stationary. However, in respect of sound locators, it is the locator itself that is trained around to register the best sound emission from the target.

Early development would again take us back to the First World War and 'sound trumpets' and then follow roughly the same route as disc research and sound mirrors. Certainly sound locators were tried at SEE on Woolwich Common, as can be seen in one of the illustrations, but the research and development soon migrated fifteen miles to the south to ADEE, Biggin Hill. However, as with the sound mirror field work being undertaken on the south coast, a lot of practical work involving sound locators was undertaken remote from Biggin Hill, in this case at Orford Ness (sometimes appears in documents as Orfordness) on the east coast.

The theory was that a sound locator unit would work in conjunction with a searchlight team. The prime function for the sound locators was to pinpoint the source of engine noise at night and when the operators were confident they would call out the bearing and altitude of the target and give the order, 'On'. This would bring the searchlight (or projector as it is often referred to in documents of the time) into play to illuminate the target, ready for a defending fighter to engage it or, later, AA guns to open up. A simple theory but much work had to be undertaken to improve the reception of the sound and to deal with practicalities which may not be immediately obvious,

One of the parallel developments, this one by the Japanese. Very similar in design to some of the French systems, its name translates from the Japanese as 'War Horns'. Little is know of the efficiency of this system or how it progressed but does have the look of a contraption that might have been the work of the fertile imagination of the cartoonist, William Heath-Robinson.
(Courtesy of the Royal Artillery Historical Trust)

An interesting pair of pictures of an unfortunate German Shepherd dog named 'Asti' who was used to test the effects on its ability to identify the direction of a sound source. Binaural (both ears) accurately located the source, one ear provided poor directional location.(Courtesy of the Royal Artillery Historical Trust)

spoiled as we have been by the immediacy and easy accessibility of RADAR. For instance, there was the requirement to off-set the position given by the sound locator to take into account the time lag generated by the speed of sound. Obviously the sound locator was registering the sound of the aircraft from a position it occupied some seconds earlier, and this would vary with the distance from the target and the relative angle at which the sound was being intercepted. For example, if a Bristol Fighter was flying at 9,000ft at right angles to the sound locator, over a track two miles from the locator the sound would have to travel 2.6 miles. In round figures, it will take 12 seconds to reach to locator in which time the fighter, flying at, say 115 mph, will have travelled about 1/3 of a mile (.5km) before the sound reached the locator.

Thus an early part of the research and development, almost certainly undertaken at ADEE Biggin Hill, was to develop a scale to off-set such errors. A simple visual sight was fitted, by which a third member of a three-man team took sightings through a back sight, quoting the actual bearing of the

An early sound locator, designed by Handford whilst the Signals Experimental
Establishment was still at Woolwich Common. Also in the background can be
seen another variation of the flat, twin-skinned sound disc, similar to that trialled
at Joss Gap and which later became the model for both the Biggin Hill and
Romney Marsh Sytems.
(Courtesy of the Royal Artillery Historical Trust)

target from a scale indicated on the 'leading edge' of the ring or stirrup foresight (see illustrations). He would move the foresight closer or further away when the speed of the aircraft had been estimated, along a scale with speed in mph etched into the supporting arm.

The three-man team required for the Sound Locator Mark III had three distinctly different jobs. Number 1 in the team directed the locator through azimuth i.e. through the horizontal plane to obtain the peak noise level and register the bearing. Number 2 was then responsible for elevating the system to better improve the volume of the reception and Number 3 would then operate sights for time lag correction. To avoid too many clashes of physical input Number 1 always had priority. As Tucker put it, 'The azimuth listener must be correct before the altitude listener can function satisfactorily; the azimuth listener is, so to speak, the senior partner.' This, in turn led to the development and provision of a sighting scale for azimuth and altitude for fitting to searchlights, to be able to use the information provided by the sound locator team. Initially, searchlights were simply used as a rather blunt instrument to be panned around in the hope of illuminating a small moving target in a very big dark sky.

Practical field trials at Orford Ness began to reflect that the sound locator system would add greatly to the defence potential. As early as 1918 Navy Lieutenant Milne (RNVR) recorded those trials using a Bristol Fighter had yielded very positive results over a period of an hour and twenty minutes. Two 24 inch (60 cm) projectors were used and the fighter was illuminated on 24 occasions, the lights having been guided by the locator team. The observer in the Bristol Fighter had good background experience of searchlight operations and commented that the results were, '...extraordinarily good'.

At the core of the Mk III Sound Locator was the Handford Trumpet, designed by Tucker's close colleague who also had also been deeply involved at ADEE, Biggin Hill, and who was Tucker's deputy at the field testing sites at Hythe and Dungeness. The Mk III Locator indicated the way ahead and was the basis for the development of numerous subsequent designs. It was not only trialled on land but Handford Trumpet locators were installed in the gunnery tender attached to HMS Excellent for sea trials. In an Admiralty record (ADM 186/259) dated 1922 and 1923 is recorded:

Early days of sound location at Biggin Hill. Field trials of locators in the grounds of Squerryes Court, Westerham. Two separate units are used with stethoscopes, one for azimuth (left to right in the horizontal), and one in elevation (up and down in the vertical). These two operations were to be combined on one unit at the next development stage.(Courtesy of the Royal Artillery Historical Trust)

Squerryes Court, Westerham again with the operators clearly scanning different planes, vertical and hoizontal. (Courtesy of the Royal Artillery Historical Trust)

C.B. 1640
Progress in
Gunnery material
1922 and 1923

8. Location of Aeroplanes by Sound. – Considerable research in the location of aeroplanes by sound has been carried out during the past year, and investigation of the various problems is continuing.

The most promising instruments are:

(a)   Handford trumpet locators.

(b)   10ft disc (microphone system) sound locator.

   The above instruments are described in detail in C.B. 1577 (1). Page 40 etc.

It has been approved to carry out sea-going trials with these two systems in the gunnery tender attached to HMS "Excellent." (G.01523/22).

The Mk 1 Sound Locator which is using the design which would prevail throughout subsequent developments. Unlike the horns shown at Squerryes Court all four are now arranged on one post. The top and bottom horns on the left are for elevation and that in the middle left, and to the right, are for azimuth. First development of the sighting scale is on top of the post. (Courtesy of the Royal Artillery Historical Trust)

Thus the design and development work being done at ADEE, Biggin Hill, was cross-service and, as we will see later, international. In 1925 another field test of note was associated with the Navy. It was proposed that if sound locator equipment could be mounted successfully on ships, the location of the listening post, and thus the distance away from the shore where incoming raiders could be detected could be extended, establishing defence pickets at sea. Thus ADEE staff engaged in a series of exchanges of requests and reports to have equipment fitted to Admiralty Drifter, HMD Lunar Bow.

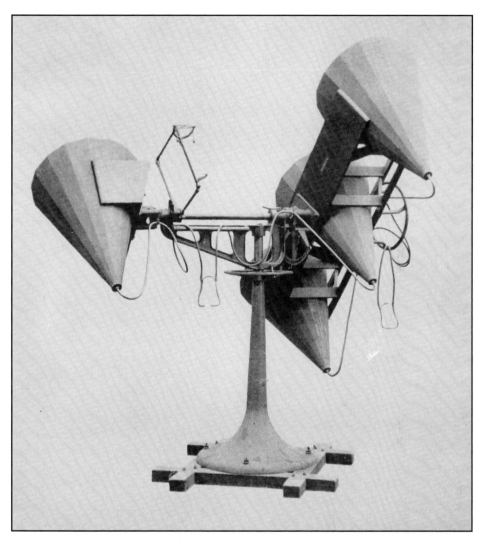

Mk 1 Sound Locator from the rear. An interesting and informative image which appears to have been cut out from its original background. It shows clearly the arrangement of the sound tubes and stethoscopes as well as the ranging from above the azimuth bar, together with the styrup-shaped scale. A large piece of equipment which was soon to be refined at Biggin Hill with no loss of efficiency. (National Archive)

The Mk 2 Sound Locator at Biggin Hill. This is using the Handford trumpets and the (relatively) crude arrangement of stethoscopes can be observed hanging from the frame. This, as described in the text, was operated by a three man crew, one operating the azimuth, one the elevation and the third man operating the stirrup fitting on the speed scale visually. In the background can be seen a chestnut paling fence which separated the War Office site from the active aerodrome and will be observed in many of the illustrations which follow, demonstrating that they were taken at ADEE Biggin Hill.
(Courtesy of the Royal Artillery Historical Trust)

A Mk 3 Sound Locator from the rear, taken at Biggin Hill. Again the tubes connecting the Handford trumpets to the stethoscopes can be observed. This unit differs from the first illustration in that it has a tripod stand for the first time and an optical sight. (Courtesy of the Royal Artillery Historical Trust).

A nice posed shot of Army personnel, complete with puttees, steel helmets and respirators. The man in the middle grasps the horizonal bar and turns it to locate the source of the sound, whilst his 'Number 2' grasps the elevation bar. Number 3 prepares to read off from the scale. It is also worthy of note that the simple stethoscope has now morphed in a more substantial headsets. (Courtesy of the Royal Artillery Historical Trust)

Shot from a different angle to demonstrate the Number 2 operating the elevation arm by use of a stirrup in front. Presumably to offer the opportunity to work in a confined space. (Courtesy of the Royal Artillery Historical Trust)

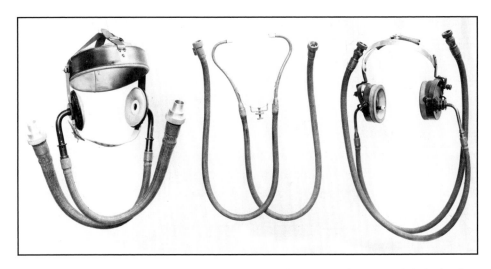

The progress of the headset. In the middle is the early Mk 2 stethoscope, right is the first development of that, the Mk 3 headset, and to the left is the more substantial, and probably more comfortable Mk 4 set. (Courtesy of the Royal Artillery Historical Trust)

She was berthed at the Arsenal Pier, Woolwich, and a sixteen foot long sound collecting horn and paraboloid mirror were installed. Dr Tucker, Percy Rothwell and other members of the Biggin Hill technical staff were very much involved in the trials, which operated out of Dover, and the results added to the now substantial pool of knowledge carrying sound location forward.

By the end of the 1920s and on into the 1930s the research was being honed into three main fields as the Romney Marsh disc system gradually came to the end of its useful life. Gun ranging was still developing on the War Office site, but our main threads extending from ADEE, Biggin Hill, were the sound mirrors at Hythe, Dungeness and Folkestone, and the sound locators, in particular the prospect of efficient mobile units, were being planned. This would produce equipment which would play an important role in WW 2.

For experimental purposes, a large fixed sound locator was constructed at ADEE, Biggin Hill. It was fitted with the now common paraboloids which were of cast aluminium and 3ft wide at the mouth. As previously mentioned, the paraboloid or parabolic reflector not only concentrated a very directional beam of sound onto the collector but also tended to screen out superfluous background noise. The huge new unit was also to be fitted with hand wheels and gears so that the operation could be more precise. As large as it was, the research unit was also to form the basis of a fixed installation which might feature in key locations but the research was still firmly towards the effective development of mobile units. These would, as they successfully had, work in conjunction with searchlights and investigations were made into a system called 'ARC' (Automatic Remote Control). This, it was proposed, would eventually link the locator with a searchlight and the movements of the locator would be automatically shadowed by the searchlight by means of an electrical step motor until the order 'On' was given. This was later to be adapted for anti-aircraft guns before, eventually, RADAR guided guns became a reality.

Dr Tucker, as Superintendent of Acoustic Research, was keen that the new technology should proceed with new equipment specifically designed for the job. For instance, rather than press an existing design of trailer, like that available to carry a searchlight, into use for the mobile sound locators, he insisted that the trailer should be a new, job-specific design. This is demonstrated by a request from the Superintendent of ADEE, then a Major Edwards, for four covers (tyres) and tubes for Morris wheels for a trailer that was being constructed for an experimental sound locator.

By 1931 the Superintendent of the ADEE was able to reassure the Royal Engineers Board that a new mobile unit was under trial at the Biggin Hill Establishment and when used with a standard 36 inch (90 cm) searchlight was achieving very good results. The sound locator consisted of two parts - as essentially did the early Handford units – i.e., the sound locators and the sighting unit. Of the four sound collectors, two were used in azimuth to determine the direction from which the sound was coming, and the second two to determine the angle of inclination or elevation. Of the three-man crew (or 'numbers' as they were termed – military jargon which probably springs from gun crews), one and two operated the azimuth and elevation whilst three (the 'sighting number') operated the sighting unit. This was of a more sophisticated design than that on the Handford Mk III but, essentially, did the same thing. Taking into account the estimated speed of the target, the unit found the course automatically and from that information took into account the time lag; essentially finding a line of sight from a line of sound.

At the end of the year, trials were held at Biggin Hill with a Hawker Horsley flying in the vicinity of the aerodrome and WO site. The results reported were encouraging:

> Aircraft at 10,000 ft, speed 100 mph, illuminated on eight runs from fourteen - visibility poor.

A week later:

> Aircraft at 6,000 ft, speed 100 mph, illuminated nine out of nine runs – visibility good.

The next night:

> Aircraft at 9,500 ft, speed 100 mph, illuminated three times out of three – visibility good.

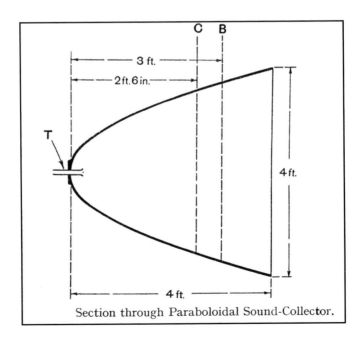

Section through Paraboloidal Sound-Collector.

The huge research system installed at Biggin Hill. Still operated by a three man
crew it was precision operated by hand wheels and gears.
(Courtesy of the Royal Artillery Historical Trust)

This obviously meant that the mobile sound locators were a viable and intrinsic part of the location and illumination of aircraft at night. Development therefore continued a pace at ADEE, Biggin Hill whilst other developments also began to be trialled.

Large horns had not entirely lost their place in the sound locator inventory. Different from paraboloids, they simply funnelled sound down to the listener. However, research showed that they were more efficient at collecting the lower tones (longer wave lengths – below 100 cycles) and could

This is an important image from the research at Biggin Hill. First it shows work underway on an optical range finder which is mounted on a scratch-built trailer. In the background, to the left, can be seen a Westland Wallace, several of which worked both with acoustic research as well as with the Anti-Aircraft School. Right of that can be observed the stunted poles and insulators which carried telephone wires which, whilst they might have been at a height as to reduce problems with aircraft, they seem to be at an ideal height to cause damage to the throat of any unwary pedestrian. Lastly, just to the left of the unit can be seen the 'Saltbox' (also inset), an important landmark to fix the position from which the image was taken. (Courtesy of the Royal Artillery Historical Trust)

thus often pick up an approaching aircraft at a greater distance than the now standard paraboloids. Because they could be used to sweep larger areas of sky somewhat quicker than the exacting paraboloid units, it was claimed to be less fatiguing for the operators.

These new designs were called 'Pilot Locators' and could log the azimuth bearing of an approaching aircraft easily before the paraboloid units could be brought to bear. This would allow the sound locator crew to be ready to register a contact with the raider as soon as it came in range, rather than having to scan around searching for it. This, of course, improved the efficiency of the locators and extended the detection range. In early experiments at ADEE the main locator was positioned near Brasted Railway Station, and the Pilot Locator about half a mile ahead of it and in contact, either wireless or field telephone.

Evidence that initial trials of the proposed linking of the locator systems direct with anti-aircraft guns also exists. In July 1936, sound locators were set up at Westerham and Brasted (south-south-east and south-east respectively of Biggin Hill), together with a Kine Theodolite to observe what was probably a theoretical trajectory of a shell. The Kine or Cine Theodolite was a variation on the surveyor's theodolite which incorporated a cine camera (developments of which are still in use today). It produced film from which the trajectory and therefore likely proximity of a shell to a target could be observed. Whether actual 3" (76 mm) shells were fired during the trials or if it was simply a tracking exercise based on the target and the read outs from the ARC equipment is unclear. Personally, I seriously doubt it would have involved live firing, which was normally reserved for the ranges such as Watchet in West Somerset.

But we have moved slightly ahead of ourselves in he story of the sound locator and, to nail dates to the time line, we need to refer, not for the first or last time, to the minutes of Prof. (later Sir) Henry Tizards's Committee for the Scientific Survey of Air Defence (CSSAD). We will return to this important committee, its constitution and effect on many things Biggin Hill-related later, but for the moment we need just to dip into the odd minute to both sample official attitudes to what was happening within a degree of isolation at ADEE, and to fix it on the time line. At the third meeting of the

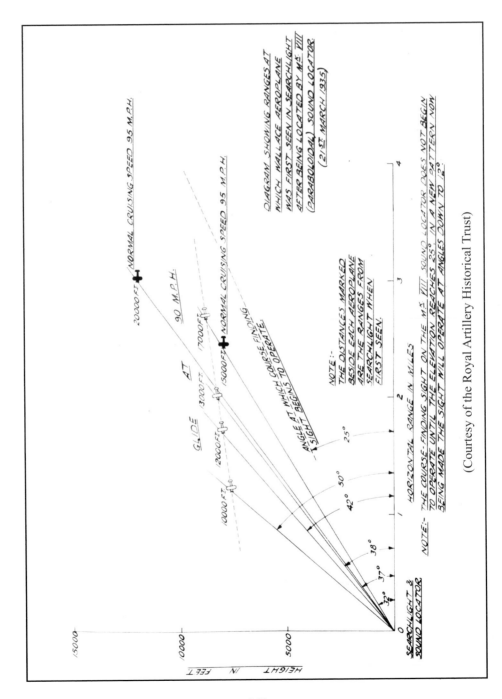

(Courtesy of the Royal Artillery Historical Trust)

Committee at the Air Ministry on 4 March 1935, the first mention of Biggin Hill is found. In this respect the subject is the effectiveness of anti-aircraft guns, and Colonel JU Hope and Captain FG Wrisberg represented the Director of Artillery at the War Office. Captain Wrisberg informed the com-

A 'Pilot Locator'(see following text) being assembled at Biggin Hill. As can be seen by the chalk markings it weighs in at 32cwt - just over 1.5 tons (1.6 tonnes).
(Courtesy of the Royal Artillery Historical Trust)

The assembled unit awaiting trials. It could be operated from either side as will be seen
in the next image. Note the bicycles in a rack under the shelves.
(Courtesy of the Royal Artillery Historical Trust)

The 'Pilot Locator' mounted on a trailer at Biggin Hill. The chestnut paling fence and low level telephone wires once again appear in the background. These units were designed to detect longer wave lengths and possibly give earlier warning.
(Courtesy of the Royal Artillery Historical Trust)

mittee that following extensive trials at Biggin Hill, he considered that there was no difficulty, in clear weather, in locating aircraft by visual means, up to about 12,000 feet (3,650 m).

The summary of Cpt. Wrisberg's input was that in his view the 3" AA gun then in use was an accurate means of delivering a shell. The major errors in AA fire lay with unreliable fuse operation and inaccurate prediction of the target to position the shell accurately. The Vickers Predictor, a complex piece of equipment by any measure, which was then coming into use was

A fixed 'Pilot Locator' at Biggin Hill. The bracket protruding about half way up the central column was to allow another operator, or the single operator, to sit facing the opposite direction. The azimuth scale can be read off the at the base and the elevation is on a quadrant just under the horns. (Courtesy of the Royal Artillery Historical Trust)

capable of setting up the gun to deliver the shell more accurately and it was thought that when the 3.7" (94 mm) gun came into wider use, the clockwork fuse which would replace the powder fuse in the 3" shell would be more accurate. The Committee Chairman, Henry Tizard, who had had experience of anti-aircraft guns and the development of fuses in WW I, asked a question on the general efficiency of the 3" gun at 15,000 feet (4,570 m) and was told the rather bald fact that, in Cpt. Wrisberg's view, the first group of shells would at least cause approaching aircraft to take avoiding action; but in terms of destructive power he suggested that it would take, on average, 500 shells to cause vital damage to one aircraft. He continued to report that if six 3" guns could be brought to bear, and each could fire an average of 20 shells per minute for two minutes, there was a statistical probability that they had a 50% chance of causing vital damage to one aircraft; a rather prosaic condemnation of the value, at the time, of anti-aircraft guns in destroying bomber formations. However, the role of the anti-aircraft gun was not limited to the first-hand destruction of aircraft, it also played an important role in the breaking up of formations of bombers to make them more vulnerable to fighter attack; a deterrent effect on the morale of bomber crews, who would sometimes turn back in the face of sustained heavy fire, or at least fall short of reaching their target. In reverse, the positive effects of anti-aircraft fire on the morale of the civilian population were completely disproportionate to its actual military value.

What could be a Kine Theodolite in use at Biggin Hill. This would be in what is now East Camp, looking back south-west towards the area now occupied by the Rizon Jet hangar. The tent and buildings to the left are part of the acoustic testing field and to the right is the main hangar. (Courtesy of the Royal Artillery Historical Trust)

Another view of what
might have been the
Kine Theodolite men-
tioned in the text. This
view is across the
aerodrome towards the
boundary with what
remained of Cudham
Lodge Farm.
(Courtesy of the Royal
Artillery Historical
Trust)

Where the ADEE at Biggin Hill would come into this would be in the
complex experiments to improve the visual location of high flying aircraft
and overcome problems such as blue sky scatter and the inefficiencies of
the human eye in focusing on small objects against a bright background. If
these could be overcome, and the altitude, course and speed of the aircraft
could be accurately obtained, the Vickers Predictor seemed capable of getting shells close to their target; the development of optical range finding
was therefore another crucial function based at ADEE Biggin Hill.

Sound locator research, already well established at Biggin Hill, was con-
tinuing to improve, but in the minutes of Tizard's first meeting of the
CSSAD (28 January 1935) are recorded the DSR's (Director of Scientific
Research at the Air Minstry - HE Wimperis) comments are recorded:

DSR said that excellent results had been obtained at 10,000 feet in the directing of searchlights by trumpet sound locators. Owing, however, to increased aircraft speeds and to advances in the art of silencing he considered that sound location must be relied upon to a decreasing extent.

The Committee appreciated that, in a few years' time, sound location may often be ineffective and that it is therefore of great importance to consider other means of detection.

However, some cognizance of the increases of speeds of aircraft had been taken into account and trials at Biggin Hill had substituted the Handley Page Heyford, a redundant bi-plane bomber, for an Avro Anson from No. 48 Sqn. Not a huge step forward but at least the Anson was of a modern twin engine design and flew at 188 mph (302 kph) compared to the lumbering Heyford, which could manage 140 mph (224 kph) on a good day. Whether it was a delayed response to an enquiry by Tizard, or due to further comments being made regarding the practical application of sound locators is unknown, but Tucker wrote to Tizard in 1936 to assure him that they had been able to il-luminate an Anson flying at 20,000 ft (6,100 m) - more or less its service ceiling - on eight out of eight occasions. Later, also in 1936, Tucker reported back on ADEE experiments with sound locators positioned at Titsey and Brasted and involving three Gloster Gauntlets of No. 32 Sqn, Biggin Hill (of whom we will hear more soon). This was definitely moving up a grade as the Gauntlet fighters could top 230 mph (370 kph) and had a service ceil-ing of 33,500 ft (10,200 m).

There is no doubt that the equipment designed and sometimes built at Biggin was of the highest quality precision engineering, as some of the illustrations will show. Particularly impressive is the course-finding sight which is illustrated and which looks hugely complex, but to have been of any practical use must have been relatively simple to use in the field. The purpose of the sight was to compensate for the time lag caused by the line of sound/line of sight equation produced by the (relatively) slow speed of sound. The course-finding sight illustrated shows the sighting rod which physically points to the target, above that is the metal bow and over both is located the prismatic binocular telescope which was viewed through a right angle. Apparently the metal bow had to be aligned with the sighting rod and a projection under the bow, which can be seen in the illustration (which follow), was called the follower pin and could be aligned by touch in the dark.

Sound locators certainly had a future and the team at ADEE were constantly trying to improve the performance of the equipment. One thing which stood out was the varying ability of listeners to locate and track sounds. Some seem to grasp the idea in seconds and have the ability to focus their attention on the pinpoint of sound in their head, whilst others seemed vague and found it difficult to maintain concentration; thus it was proposed that a visual display might improve matters. For this expert help was brought in and the paraboloids from a Mk IX locator were sent to EMI (Electrical and Mechanic Industries – later a leader in producing a wide range of music on vinyl) at their HQ in Blythe Road, Hayes, Middlesex (now Hillingdon). Their brief was to fit sensitive microphones at the focus of the paraboloids. These would be tuned to a range of sound most common to aero engines, from a wave length of 1.3 m to .3 m; although lower tones at longer wave lengths were also generated it was beyond the capacity of the portable sound locators to capture them. The signal would be amplified and fed to an oscilloscope where a wave pattern would be generated making it easy to scan for the peak signal. A very similar system was later to receive the return signals for RADAR, a scene with which readers will be familiar from documentaries. As a side issue, it is always worth keenly watching these film clips, having first donned the traditional anorak, as from time to time the scene is not of a mobile RADAR unit, as the commentary would have it, but of the incoming signal from a sound locator.

By the beginning of the Second Ward War, mobile sound locators were ready to play a major role in the defence of the realm, particularly at night. With RADAR essentially only looking out from the coast and the Observer Corps essentially blind at night, there was little to guide the searchlights other than the sound locators. They were, therefore, an essential part of the eventual successful defence against the onslaught of the Luftwaffe and would not be replaced until more sophisticated RADAR came into use, in particular, the AI set mounted in airborne night fighters and, later, the GCI

(Ground Controlled Interception) system on which my dad worked in the latter days of WW 2.

The mobile sound locator was the direct decedent of the early gun ranging of WW I and owed much of its development to the genius of Dr William Sansome Tucker and his hand-picked team at the Air Defence Experimental Establishment at Biggin Hill. Without this development Britain would have been a great deal more vulnerable during its hours of greatest need; just one small component of the Battle of Britain and the Blitz for which Biggin Hill was responsible; it wouldn't be the only one.

Footnote: Orford Ness was taken over by the War Office in 1913 for secret experimentation. The area had been drained and an airfield laid out and, during WW I, much development work was done on bomb and machine gun sights, as well as parachutes and photography. It remained in WO hands, being used for nuclear experiments, until 1971 and is now largely a wild life reserve.

The Mk V1 course-finding sight showing the sighting rod which physically points to the target, above that is the metal bow and over both is located the prismatic binocular telescope, viewed through a right angle. The metal bow had to be aligned with the sighting rod and a projection under the bow, which can be seen in the illustration, was called the follower pin and could be aligned by touch in the dark.
(Courtesy of the Royal Artillery Historical Trust)

Assembling a Mk VI unit at Biggin Hill in 1933. The aerodrome is beyond
the chestnut paling fence which seems to have been bolstered by a steel railing fence.
It is amazing how sophisticated these detectors had become, with more development
yet to come, acoustic detection was still the only means of locating enemy aircraft,
particularly in the dark (the first records of the concept and early experiments on
RADAR do not appear for a further 2 years). The development of sound
detectors can be best appreciated by the series of pictures that follow.
(Courtesy of the Royal Artillery Historical Trust)

IMAGES OF THE DEVELOPMENT OF THE SOUND LOCATOR

Above: Sound ranging laboratory and trials field at Biggin Hill. Below: using an early locator in the test field. (Courtesy of the Royal Artillery Historical Trust)

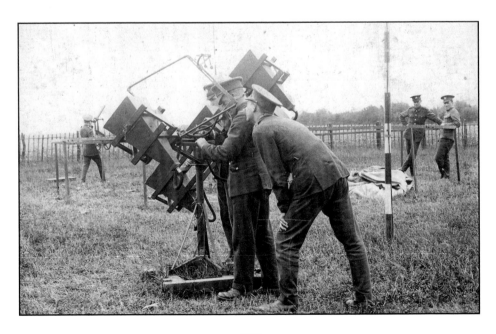

Early sound location system on trial at Biggin Hill. Handford trumpets in a slightly different arrangement to what would become the Mk III. Left to right Bill Allen and Fred Jessup.
(Courtesy of the Royal Artillery Historical Trust)

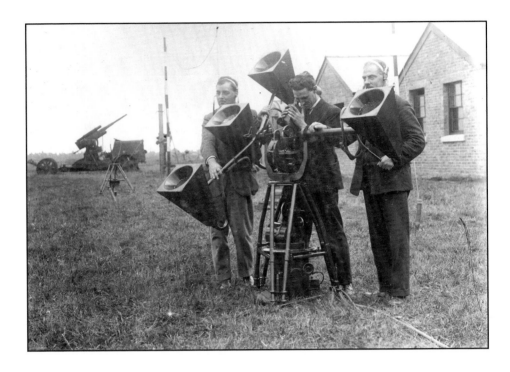

Above: Further development of the sound locator, note AA Gun to the rear.
Left to right, E French, G Chance, L Walker.
(Courtesy of the Royal Artillery Historical Trust)

Above, a very interesting picture which shows, to the rear, the hangar which was used by the Night Flying Flight on the airfield. This is a complete setup of a Mk III sound locator linked to a searchlight. In between is an optical range finder. The person far left is unknown, but the group to the right are, in front, A Searby, behind, left to right, E French, G Chance & J Walker.
(Courtesy of the Royal Artillery Historical Trust)

Above: Searchlight (or projector) surrounded by an azimuth scale and linked to an optical sight. Below: The same system in the field on the Western Front, west of Bethune. (Courtesy of the Royal Artillery Historical Trust)

Searchlight (projector) on the trials field at Biggin Hill. Cables leading away
suggest it is linked to an optical sight or a sound locator.
(Courtesy of the Royal Artillery Historical Trust)

Searchlight research was all part of the work undertaken at the Air Defence
Experimental Establishment (ADEE), Biggin Hill. This is the same searchlight
as the previous illustration, but from the left to show other features.
(Courtesy of the Royal Artillery Historical Trust)

A Mk 6 searchlight in the area of the acoustic test field. It is being aimed the operator who walks the bar around for azimuth (bearing) and operates the wheel for elevation. The Mk 6 was successfully linked to sound locators and powered by electric step motors to find the target by means of acoustics. This provided a very successful combination during the Blitz, illuminating numerous targets for the gunners that wounds otherwise have simply been stabs in the dark.

Crossley lorry of the Air Defence Experimental Establishment (ADEE) Biggin Hill on the Acoustic Test Field with searchlight onboard. The canvass tilt would normally be put into place over the equipment, and the Sound Locator would be hitched up for towing to the site in the proximity of the Anti-Aircraft guns. Much skill was required to site the Sound Locators in a position far enough away from the guns as not to have their listening stream lost in the reports of the guns, but close enough for good communications.

(Courtesy of the Royal Artillery Historical Trust)

Mr A Searby operating an optical sighting unit outside the laboratory on the trials field. (Courtesy of the Royal Artillery Historical Trust)

A slightly different arrangement of the four sound collectors in a square format. No special reference was found to this variation in official documents. (Courtesy of the Royal Artillery Historical Trust)

The square four arrangement with electronic controls linked to the position correcting sight. The controls would have been linked to a searchlight which would have imitated the movements of the sound locator. (Courtesy of the Royal Artillery Historical Trust)

Another example of the apparently short lived square four design. This obvously a more substantially mounted unit, probably for research at ADEE. The steel fencing is in evidence which seems to have come into use on the site in the early thirties.
(Courtesy of the Royal Artillery Historical Trust)

The four square variation, this time mounted on a trailer for mobility. On the back of the trailer what appears to be a more complex course correction system.

(Courtesy of the Royal Artillery Historical Trust)

Fred Jessup fitting the optics the course corrector on a Mk VIII Sound Locator.

(Courtesy of the Royal Artillery Historical Trust)

Partially assembled course corrector. The quality of precision engineering on these pieces of equipment is staggering. (Courtesy of the Royal Artillery Historical Trust)

Mk VIII Sound Locator from the front, quite a business-like piece of equipment which yielded some very accurate results. Below, the same unit from the rear.

(Courtesy of the Royal Artillery Historical Trust)

Two views of the Mk VIII unit ready to deploy to its site. The searchlight and associated equipment would be within the tilt at the rear of lorry so as to come as a single unit. The lettering on the driver's door records: Air. Def. Exp. Est. (Air Defence Experimental Establishment [Biggin Hill]). (Courtesy of the Royal Artillery Historical Trust)

Another unit hitched to a Crossley, ready to deploy. In this image the seachlight can clearly be seen inside the canvass tilt.

(Courtesy of the Royal Artillery Historical Trust)

Mk VIII Sound Locator in MT (Motor Transport) Section.
(Courtesy of the Royal Artillery Historical Trust)

Mk VIII Sound Locator with transitional works being undertaken behind.
To the rear right is Bessonneau canvass hangar, and to the left the structural
steel of a more modern and permanent building is in evidence.
(Courtesy of the Royal Artillery Historical Trust)

The rear of the Mk VIII, revealing another view of the developing aerodrome.
Huts to the rear left appear to be associated with contruction work as the name
'Wimpey's' appears in bold lettering on the side.

(Courtesy of the Royal Artillery Historical Trust)

The Mk IX was the development of the Sound Locator which was to be produced in large numbers. In many respects it incorporated the most technical advances in acoustic detection and was the result of nearly twenty years work at ADEE, Biggin Hill.
In this image the standard three man crew still operates the unit but by precision gearing and hand wheels, rather than moving the paraboloids by hand.
The 'number' on the top of the unit is operating the course corrector and his hand can be seen to be on the bow, his thumb on the follower pin. As described earlier in the text this allowed the corrector to be used by touch in the dark.
This is described as the 'Action Position' with road wheels removed and the unit supported on jacks and what appear to be thick rubber cushes.
(Courtesy of the Royal Artillery Historical Trust)

Mk IX unit from the rear showing the two operating 'numbers' in position on sprung seats.(Courtesy of the Royal Artillery Historical Trust)

Mk IX unit from the ¾ front. The road wheels are neatly stacked to the right and the cable leading away to the left is what carries instructions to the searchlight. Having strategically placed the sound locator away from the gun site to avoid too much interference from the reports of the guns, the locator itself had to be placed remote from the generator which powered the searchlight.

(Courtesy of the Royal Artillery Historical Trust)

PLATE 1

LOCATOR SOUND, Mᴷ IX. FRONT VIEW. READY FOR ACTION.

The set of images which follow are clearly for an instructional manual or report. Shot in front of the usual canvass screen, these images appear to be inside a building and shot using artifical lighting. Although shown as a Mk IX locator, 'Ready For Action', the road wheels are still in place and the jacks are being used to stabilise the chassis, rather than support it. This may be for a more rapid response with a complete mobile unit, complete with guns. (Courtesy of the Royal Artillery Historical Trust)

PLATE **2**
BACK VIEW.

Again a 'studio' image of the Mk IX Sound Locator, this time from the rear.
(Courtesy of the Royal Artillery Historical Trust)

Mk IX Sound Locator ready to move. The numbering is again indicative of the set of plates being shot for a manual or report, however that was not located with the images which were stored in an album. (Courtesy of the Royal Artillery Historical Trust)

Before leaving the Air Defence Experimental Establishment in South Camp, Biggin Hill, it is worth exposing some other images which are associated with the site, but not necessarily relevant to the core developments in acoustic research.

An interesting contraption found in the ADEE album. The only possibility which immediately presents is for the horn on top to be gathering sound from a sound mirror whilst the observer searches for the source. (Courtesy of the Royal Artillery Historical Trust)

Again from the ADEE album, a caravan developed for the Observer Corps. Above in its travelling configuration, below with dome raised - purpose completely unknown. (Courtesy of the Royal Artillery Historical Trust)

THE DEVELOPMENT OF RAF BIGGIN HILL

Towards the end of the nineteen-twenties the decision was made to expand Britain's air defence potential. It became known as 'The Expansion Period' and Biggin Hill was to upgraded to a two Squadron airfield. However, a significant factor in the delay to fund the modernisation of Biggin Hill was the main road from Bromley to Westerham in the south, which formed the western boundary of the Airfield. The original huts and hangars had been neatly contained within a strip between the road and the grass runways, and it was here that the Building Committee proposed to site the new Officers' Mess and NCOs Messes, married quarters, barracks, and other buildings. The Air Defence Staff, as practical airmen, vetoed this plan, pointing out that any building here would menace the southern flying approaches to the Airfield, and suggested that all non-operational premises should be situated on the far side of the main road. The idea of a major thoroughfare running through the heart of a military Station was an anathema to the Building Committee who countered with the suggestion that all living quarters should be moved to the north, a good two miles from the working area. However, it was discovered that houses built here could not be connected to the main sewerage system, a not unimportant point, and the Building Committee reluctantly agreed to have the Station bisected by the Westerham Road.

Twenty-nine acres of land was acquired for the new Station and had to be purchased piecemeal from several owners. Two landlords held out, however, and refused to allow their property to be incorporated into the expanding aerodrome. One, Forge Cottage, consisted of a rather dilapidated tea garden from which, from time to time, the Officer Commanding barred airmen because of a tendency for ladies of ill repute to frequent it. The other was a well-known landmark known as the Salt Box, a small building on the western periphery of the Airfield, used as a stopping place for light refreshments, very popular with cyclists and the odd charabanc outing. A petrol pump had been installed to facilitate motorists, but it was subsequently thought to be a very real fire hazard to the newly constructed hangar nearby. This was unacceptable to the Air Ministry and this, as well as the need to widen the road, made the case for purchase.

The Saltbox itself comes up often in numerous references to Biggin Hill, standing as it did on the eastern side of Main Road, opposite Saltbox Hill. Many local oral history stories attribute the name of Saltbox Hill to various progenitors such as a salt box at the top of the hill for freezing weather, to a café on the western side of the road called 'The Saltbox' (which did exist and was a great attraction to bikers of the sixties – it later became The Manor and in 2015 was developed for housing). The truth of the matter goes back much further in time to the aforesaid building which once stood in Main Road, opposite the hill. The Saltbaox was of a peculiar design and had a very steeply pitched roof, that's a fact and it can be observed in numerous photographs; what is less certain is why it was built in that way. The most prominent theory is that Earl Stanhope, who owned the land, had the house built for farm workers and, having apparently recently returned from something of an expedition to the Himalayas, said that he would show people how to build a house to stand on a windy ridge - apparently the design replicated in Main Road was common there. Locals immediately saw the resemblance to a Victorian saltbox and the name stuck.

The house was sold to William Henry Nevard in August 1914 by the Rt. Hon. James Richard Earl Stanhope of the one part and Richard Phillip Stanhope of the other part (quoted verbatim from the contract). Some local histories have this as early as 1901, and it being purchased by Nevard from a Mr Henry Piggott, but copies of the transfer documents in the National Archive bear out the later date. William Nevard ran it as a successful business and the arrival of the RFC, in late 1916, and the commencement of flying in 1917, could have done nothing but improve business; apparently there was a well-worn path to the Saltbox from the airfield. However, in the late nineteen-twenties the decision was taken to make Biggin Hill a two squadron station and part of this was to have Main Road improved to a 40 ft (12 m) carriageway. As the road bends around the site of the Saltbox the land drops away to the west and, consequently, the widening of the road had to take land to the east, and this included the land in front of the Saltbox, so negotiations began to purchase the land from William Nevard. The site was visited in September 1929 by a representative of the Air Ministry,

probably from the Works and Buildings Dept at Uxbridge, which resulted in an offer to Nevard, thought to have been around £450. Nevard protested that Air Minstry was taking his livelihood away and in a letter dated 14 November, 1929, asked for £2500 (about £142,000 in today's money). Negotiations must have dragged on because the actual conveyancing is not mentioned in Air Minstry correspondence until a letter dated November, 1930. The undated sale contract between the President of the Air Council and Mr Nevard settled the price at £2000. The Nevards moved a few hundred yards across the road to Crown Ash Cottage at the top of Saltbox Hill. For reasons lost in the mists of time, the actual eastern boundary of the site is still preserved in a kink in the perimeter fence of the airport and can be observed to this day.

The Saltbox as seen looking north; the steep raking roof is very evident, as is the land in front which was needed to widen the road on the inside of the bend. (Both Tony Lewis - Biggin Hill Then and Now).

It is interesting to note that Forge Cottage was demolished in the bombing during 1940, but Salt Box lingered into decay, finally being demolished in 1954. Fortunately, the actual extension of the Airfield itself had proved less troublesome. Originally 117 acres of Cudham Lodge Farm had been taken as the nucleus of Biggin Hill Aerodrome and, since then, more land had been added on a piecemeal basis. With the new expansion scheme, however, a doubling of the airfield land was required. The tenant of the Farm, John Westacott, was understandably reluctant to part with yet more fields, so the landlord, Lord Stanhope, proposed an outright purchase of the whole property with suitable compensation being paid to Westacott. After lengthy negotiation Cudham Lodge, (home of many families of note, the Mannings, the Braiziers, and the Waleys, who had contributed much to local history) was no more than a memory.

The Main Gate and Guardroom at Biggin Hill towards the end of
the reconstruction period but before the road widening.
(Tony Lewis - Biggin Hill Then and Now)

PLAN OF THE MAIN CAMP CIRCA 1933

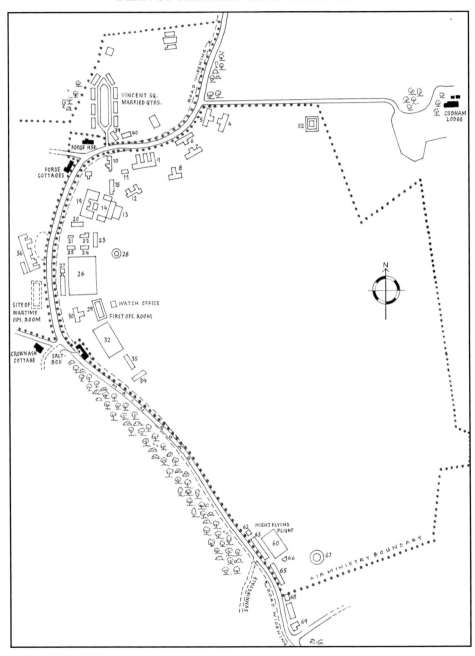

RAF BIGGIN HILL – 1933 KEY TO BUILDINGS

4	Barrack Block Design 'C'
5	Barrack Block Design 'C'
6	Barrack Block Design 'C'
7	Barrack Block Design 'C'
8	Sick Quarters
9	Combined Dining Room and Institute
10	Guard House Design 'C' (With Fire Party Access)
11	Ration Store
12	Sergeants' Mess
13	Fuel Store
14	MT Yard and Sheds
15	Airmen Pilots Quarters
19	Main Stores & Workshops
20	Armoury
21	Inflammable Store
22	Lubricant Store
23	Pilots Room, Locker Room, Airmen's Waiting Room
24	Parachute Store
25	Test House (two Bays)
26	Aeroplane Shed (Tripple Bay)
27	Workshops
28	Compass Platform
29	Operations Block
30	Office Block (Stn HQ)
32	'F' Type Shed
33	Pilots Room, Locker Room, Airmen's Waiting Room
34	MG Test Butt
35	W & B Yard (Without Section Office)
36	Officers' Mess & Quarters
52	Bulk Petrol Installation (Aviation)

Night Flying Section

60	Aeroplane Shed
62	Blacksmith's Shop
63	Woodwork Shop
64	Dope Shop
65	Officers' Mess
66	Petrol Installation
67	Compass Platform
68	Battery House
69	Power House

Note: Buildings missing from the numerical list are not shown because they were too widely dispersed to show on this plan, or were of no immediate interest, like tennis courts, latrines, emergency water supplies or fire tanks.

The new Officers' Mess for RAF Biggin Hill.Observing the rather raw state of the driveway would tend to indicate this was soon after completion, probably before first occupation. (Tony Lewis - Biggin Hill Then and Now)

CHAPTER SEVEN

MIRRORS TO THE WALL

The Decline of Acoustic Research

The second major limb of sound research, the sound mirrors (the Hythe System as it was designated) was still improving and offering good results. The 'system' included the mirror at Abbot's Cliff, the two mirrors at Hythe, and the two mirrors and 200ft wall at Dungeness. Information was fed from all three sites to a control room at Hythe where it was filtered and turned into a cohesive plot. The control room itself was probably one of the huts built on the site as there is some conjecture as to whether or not the surviving concrete bunker was there before WW 2, and may have had nothing to do with the Acoustic Research Station.

After thirteen years of development under the watchful eye of ADEE, Biggin Hill, the system was beginning to approach something of a zenith and was brought into play for the annual Air Defence of Great Britain exercises between 1931 and 1935. ADEE itself was also developing and was the central establishment for further anti-aircraft research. In his seminal work on acoustics, 'Echoes From the Sky' - Richard Scarth quotes from a memorandum which demonstrates that ADEE, Biggin Hill, was very much in the centre of things. Dated 1934 it reads:

'Notes for Superintendent, Air Defence Experimental Establishment

The ADEE is correctly named and allows for extension beyond mere guns and searchlights into wider regions of air defence from an Air Defence of Great Britain point of view, including early warning, handling of Observer Corps, communications and accessories to Air Defence of Great Britain Headquarters. On the scientific side, other forms of radiation than sound may require investigation and development, and this must be co-ordinated with existing schemes. The staff capable of developing this work is within ADEE already.'

Indeed all services were represented at Biggin Hill, with the army's interest being in all matters anti-aircraft (including the Anti-Aircraft School) and acoustic gun ranging; the RAF's prime interest in the detection of inbound hostiles as early as possible; and even the Navy commissioned work, a budget of some £1500 per annum being ploughed into research at Biggin Hill by the Admiralty. Their interest was in sound locators to both forewarn ships of the approach of an aerial attack, but also to detect surface craft approaching their shipping. Tests at Dungeness had proved that some of the mirror equipment was quite adept at picking up the low frequency pulses generated by ships' propellers. There was also the obvious application of establishing standing pickets some miles from the shore which, when equipped with sound locators, would effectively extend the range of detection.

With little alternative forms of early warning, the science of acoustic detection continued to develop and refine (though the first hints of an alternative system were revealed in the memorandum above and other documents). Although some aspects of the performance of the system were subject to criticism by senior air officers, Dr Tucker was quick to point out that the existing system was experimental and not tactical. He felt that if the system he had specified for the Thames Estuary could be built, it would offer all that was hoped of it. Certainly something had to be done because one of the key experimental sites was already under threat. The writing was on the wall, so to speak, at Dungeness as the coast road continued to creep further south, apparently in breach of agreements made between the developers, the owners of the nature reserve, and the War Office. Housing followed the road and between the mirrors and the sea a holiday camp (now Romney Sands Holiday Park) was being built. Consideration was being given to moving of the site further south, nearer the tip of the Dungeness peninsular, to roughly the area now occupied by the power station, but nothing was resolved before change overtook such plans.

Further developmental work was not necessary for the Thames Estuary system to be built and commissioned; thereafter research and development could take place 'on the job' as it were. The system would consist of seven sites, with 200ft walls and 30ft mirrors at the northern and southern ends of the system, and a further five 30ft mirrors, equally spaced between the two huge concrete 'bookends' to establish an overlap on cover. Experimentation with the long horns which had been christened 'Pilot Locators' had led Tucker and his team to the conclusion that the 200ft walls could act as a long distance locators to produce an azimuth bearing for the 30ft mirrors, thus saving the time it took to first locate the target on the smaller unit.

Time was of the essence and one of the chief concerns of senior officers was that as aircraft speeds increased, so the advanced warning of their approach diminished. With the average detection remaining limited to ten or twelve miles, the advanced warning was not enough to be significant. The lumbering Gothas of WW I would have taken eight minutes to cover that distance, but with the development more modern aircraft, particularly light bombers, that time could be halved.

Command and control was to be via GPO lines, which for simplicity would be drawn together in a room set aside at the Carter Lane Telephone Exchange in the middle of London, near St Paul's Cathedral. This made sense at the time as there were no cables under the Thames that could be used to feed information from the northern sites to a southern control room or vice versa. It therefore seemed logical to have the control room where the existing cables came together from each side of the river. In the control room filtered information and provided coordinates which would be plotted on a large table, on which was an outline map of the Estuary. On this, wooden blocks with colour coded inserts would be moved about as information on contacts was fed in. These would be updated every five minutes, this being dictated by the corresponding coloured triangular sections around the face of a clock on which the minute hand rested at the time. First known as the colour change clock its roots may well have been with the RFC in WW I, but later designated the Sector Clock, it became a centre-piece of all RAF Operations Rooms and, arguably, was another product of ADEE, Biggin Hill.

In the meantime, acoustic detection was planned to be available at various key points in the Empire. Plans were being drawn up for 200ft strip mirrors to be installed in Malta, Gibraltar and Singapore, and to this end Dr Tucker had made a reconnaissance of Malta as early as 1933, and Dr Paris had visited Singapore. Tucker had set out five sites for Malta with two of them positioned on each side of Grand Harbour, Valletta, at Maghtab and Zonkor, to monitor the approaches from the island of Sicily, just sixty miles to the north. A team from ADEE, Biggin Hill was to be sent out to fit out and commission the listening equipment once the wall and infrastructure were in place. The construction was to take place over the winter of 1934/35 and the first mirror, that at Maghtab, was scheduled to be ready for trials and training by the summer; indeed the Biggin Hill team were briefed to be ready for departure in June, but it was postponed until September. In the meantime key military personnel who would man the Malta mirror had had the opportunity to work up on the equipment at Dungeness in preparation for their departure.

Construction was completed in August and Messrs Ferguson and Handford from Biggin Hill were on site by 2 September. They expressed themselves happy with the construction and were soon able to complete the technical fit out and commence the test programme. The results were very good, giving a maximum range of detection of up to 37 miles (60 km) in ideal conditions and an average of 21-25 miles (34–40 km) for the majority of the time. Enquiries were also made as to the effectiveness of the strip mirror in locating naval craft which, it was confirmed, was good. The rationale behind this was, of course, that Italy was continuing to arm up and Mussolini was adopting a more and more aggressive stance, buoyed up by the increasing popularity of the Nazis in Germany. After much sabre-rattling following the so-called Walwal incident, the Italian Army had invaded Abyssinia (Ethiopia) on 3 October, 1935, demonstrating impressive military power.

With a potentially aggressive neighbour so close to Malta it was of concern that any means of detecting *MAS* boats *(Motoscafo Armoto Silurante – motor torpedo boats)* of the *Regia Marina* (Italian Navy) would be welcome. Equally, submarines running on the surface offered a very low profile in daylight and were virtually invisible at night, but the throb of their diesel engines and propeller beats might be detected by the mirrors. The MAS had been successful during WW I and had sunk at least two capital ships and the thought that they could be docked just sixty miles away in Sicily exercised the naval minds. Although opinions vary on the effectiveness of the Italian Air Force and the fighting resolve of the Army, there has always been great respect for the Italian Navy. It was confirmed by Dr Tucker that the Maghtab mirror could probably be successfully pressed into service for such a role should it become necessary, as several successful similar trials had been undertaken at Dungeness.

The 200 ft mirror at Maghtab, Malta, 1997.
(Richard Scarth by kind permission of Hilda Scarth)

The Control Room at the rear of the Maghtab mirror, taken in 1997. In considerably
better condition that its sister construction at Dungeness (see Appendix - Present Day)
(Richard Scarth by kind permission of Hilda Scarth)

The view towards the sea from the hills behind Maghtab. The 200 ft mirror,
'Il Widna' (the ear, as it is know locally) is in the middle of considerable
development on the site which is still controlled by the Maltese military.
(Richard Scarth by kind permission of Hilda Scarth)

The rear buttresses protruded through the front of the wall at Maghtab which was thought to be unacceptable and a deviation from the Dungeness design. However the break up of the Dungeness forecourt at one end has shown that the buttresses also protruded but were covered by a higher forecourt (see Appendix - Prersent Day). Below the view along the top of the wall.(Richard Scarth by kind permission of Hilda Scarth)

However, the mirror at Maghtab wasn't completely fool proof; during a visit to the mirror by General Sir Cyril Deverell, Chief of the Imperial General Staff, in February 1936, it completely failed to detect an approaching aircraft, even at very short range. This was because, conjectured Dr Paris at Biggin Hill, that the aircraft was approaching at or below 2,000ft, and at that altitude it may well have dropped below the 'acoustical horizon'. This seems to be a similar effect to that which would later apply to RADAR when targets would dissolve into what would be called 'ground returns'. Either that, or more likely, the circuitry for the microphones had failed and the listeners on the forecourt were still the early stages of training. Either way the General left the site unhappy and took the message back to the UK that he was unimpressed, to say the least.

All indications are that work ceased on the Maghtab mirror by May 1937 and, like its counterpart in Kent, it has remained in place and largely intact and it can be accessed by road, using either a car or the local bus system. Locally it is known as *Il Widna,* Maltese for 'the ear', once in the area, local people will know exactly what a visitor has come to see.

In the UK the development of the Thames Estuary System was under the watchful eye and scrutiny of Henry Tizard's Committee for the Scientific Survey of Air Defence (CSSAD) which had first met in January 1935 (more detail on this cornerstone Committee and its work is presented in Chapter 9). However, the process of developing the Estuary System continued with the sites being identified by Dr Tucker and the necessary negotiations for leasing and the ordering of materials commencing. Funding the scheme was finally approved in December 1935, but by January of the following year there comes something of a tipping point where, in a memorandum to the Superintendent of ADEE, Biggin Hill and in other exchanges, suggestions like the following were becoming more evident:

'It is by no means certain that the 200ft acoustical mirrors will be adopted for Air Defence of Great Britain purposes. The Air Ministry have not yet committed themselves on this point. We understand that the view prevailing at the moment in that Department is that such mirrors will form no part of their air defence scheme.'

Prof. Henry Tizard's CSSAD looked at acoustic detection at the first meeting.
Minuted at 3. (A) Detection is the following:

(a)   The Committee agreed that the problem of defence was largely one of detection of the position of enemy aircraft.

(b)   DSR said that excellent results had been obtained at 10,000 feet in directing searchlights by trumpet sound locators. Owing, however, to increasing aircraft speeds and to advances in the art of silencing he considered that sound location must be relied upon to a decreasing extent.

(c)   The Committee appreciated that, in a few years' time, sound location may often be ineffective and that it is therefore of great importance to consider other means of detection.

Note: DSR is the Director of Scientific Research at the Air Ministry
(HE Wimperis).

It was at the same meeting that first mention of electro-magnetic radio reflections was made, together with the name, Watson Watt. At the fifth meeting of the CSSAD, on 25 March 1935, Dr Tucker was called to give an account of acoustic research at the Air Defence Experimental Establishment, Biggin Hill and the development of equipment. A comprehensive statement on the position regarding acoustic research, prepared by Dr Tucker, was to be circulated to the committee and the notes in the minutes were intended to augment the report. However, a copy of the account was not appended to the minutes of the CSSAD and so we have to rely just on the minutes. Dr Tucker said that research was proceeding under the following headings:

(a)

 (i) Design of a Sound Locator for searchlight control.

(ii) The control of AA guns by sound location.

(iii) Prediction for barrage fire of AA guns, using the Bennet plane principle and the syntopic (sic) method.

(iv) Long distance detection with 200ft concrete mirrors.

(v) Track plotting mirrors (30ft) for the defence of the Thames Estuary.

(vi) Automatic transmission of readings for incorporation with the mirror system.

(vii) Analysis of aeroplane sounds.

(viii) Study of Metrological Acoustics.

(ix) Identification of aircraft by distinguishing the character of sound output.

Tucker went on to justify the work going on as, to all intents and purposes, at the time it was the only real option.

(b)

Dr Tucker described, and tabled a photograph of, the Mk III Sound Locator (Experimental type) of which about four hundred are in general use and two hundred are on order. The type has the advantages of cheapness and portability. Its resolving power is unsatisfactory, targets needing to be about 30 degrees apart. Direct control of searchlights is not effected; communication with the searchlight unit being by telephone. With regards to accuracy of location, Dr Tucker said that an angular accuracy of 2.5 degrees was obtained on about 40% of the times during which an aircraft is within acoustic range.
The maximum horizontal range of the Mk III Sound Locator is about six miles, though much depends on background noise. Recent tests with a Heyford aircraft fitted with the R.A.E (Griffiths) silencer, gave a maximum horizontal range of about three miles at a height of 15,000 ft.

(c)

Dr Tucker described two later types of Sound Locator, Mks VII and VIII, both of which provide for the automatic control of searchlight orientation but differ in their methods of so doing. These Locators are of the paraboloid type and are superior to the Mk III Locator in respect of magnification, resolving power and ease of use. Preliminary experiments indicate that gliding aircraft can be located under good conditions; the results of these experiments are recorded graphically in Dr Tucker's statement which is being circulated to the Committee (sadly missing from the minutes - PJO).

(d)

Dr Tucker referred to noise interference from searchlight engines and generators; to be entirely free from this interference the ground locaters would need to be half a mile distant from the searchlights. Dr Tucker referred to the technical advantages of fixed searchlight and sound locator positions; the present policy, however, provides for mobility. Much trouble was experienced in the late war when public power supply was used; the position in this respect has not been improved by the introduction of the Grid system, since direct current is essential; moreover, possible failure of the public supply must be considered.

(e)

A Pilot Sound Locator, designed for early detection rather than for accurate location, is being produced; it is of the exponential type. It has a wide acoustic field and reasonably good magnification can be obtained when it is directed at 10 or 15 degrees from the bearing of the target. Trials in quiet background conditions have shown a small increase in range over the Mk VIII Locator; in winds of 20 mph no increased range is likely to be obtained.

(f)

The following information regarding the Sound Control of AA guns augments that given in Dr Tucker's statement which is being circulated.

(h)

(i) The accuracy obtained with the Mk VII and the VIII locators in determining the line of sight for searchlight control, has led to an extension of the principle to the determination of the future line of sight for AA fire.

(ii) Trials to determine the accuracy of line of sight (but not range) have been conducted at Watchet. The results are given in Dr Tucker's statement. It was appreciated that they do not compare with the accuracy of visual methods.

(iii) Firing trials have hitherto been conducted with only one aircraft. The Chairman considered that early trials with at least two aircraft, simulating attack in different directions, should be conducted. The Committee was informed that no detailed programme for this year's trials has yet been prepared.

(iv) It was decided that the Committee should arrange to witness firing trials at Watchet during this summer.

(g)

The following information regarding long distance detection augments that given in Dr Tucker's statement which is being circulated to the Committee.

(i) Long range detection is provided by the 200ft concrete mirror; one such mirror now exists at Dungeness and two additional mirrors will be incorporated in the Thames Estuary Defence Scheme.

(ii) For heights between 4,000ft and 10,000ft an average range of 17.8 miles has been obtained for all weather conditions experienced during successive summer trials. Ranges exceeding 30 miles have occasionally been obtained; under adverse metrological conditions the maximum range has been reduced to ten miles.

(iii) The mirror is designed to have a maximum sensitivity for low range frequencies (15 to 20 ft wave length); for these wave lengths the attenuation is less than the figure of five decibels per mile associated with higher frequencies.

(iv) No organisation exists for listening throughout the year; for example with cross channel air traffic. Trials have been confined to the summer.

(v) Maximum range is limited to meteorological conditions. The 200ft mirror represents the limit of economical size and no important increase of range by sound location can be expected in the near future.

(vi) Experiments with Hart aircraft, gliding in in from a distance of 20 miles from the coast, will be conducted in May.

(vii) In adverse meteorological conditions, aircraft approaching at a height of a few hundred feet would not be detected at ranges giving any useful degree of early warning.

Dr Tucker promised to supply a programme of Acoustical experiments for 1935, when it is available.

Dr William Sansome Tucker OBE 1877-1955
(By kind permission of his granddaughter, Stephanie McMurray.)

Unfortunately, although the sites for the Thames Estuary mirrors were identified, and some had even progressed to heads of terms for the lease of land,
they were never finalised. Quick strides forward with RDF (RADAR) gave
every indication of being able to provide the distance required for effective
warning of approaching hostiles. Research, therefore, began to wind down

at Hythe and Dungeness, with key staff returning to duties at ADEE, Biggin Hill. For Dr William Samsome Tucker it must have been painful to watch funding and interest being bled away from something which had been his focus for twenty years. However all was not lost, and the development of Sound Locators was to continue to aid anti-aircraft guns and played a key role during the Battle of Britain, and especially during the German raids made under the cover of darkness which was eventually entitled the 'Blitz'.

After WW2, Dr Tucker moved to Canada to be close to his daughter, Beryl Mutton, who had a farm in Ontario. On the death of his wife he moved to the farm where he spent the rest of his life. His granddaughter, Stephanie McMurray, remembers Dr Tucker with great affection as a very humble man who never looked for recognition and whose only goal had been service to his country. (See his full Obituary by Dr Paris in the Appendices)

Note (1)

Towards the end of 1939 the move of ADEE from Biggin Hill to Christchurch, Hampshire had begun and by early 1940 it seems largely complete, being finished off by a change of designation to the Air Defence Research and Development Establishment (ADRDE). Earlier than this some members of the acoustic team like Dr Paris and Percy Rothwell had already taken up positions at Orford Ness to help develop RADAR.

Note (2)

The system set up for the use of acoustic contacts was well practised by the time the first RDF (RADAR) plots were available. It was, therefore, a section of the acoustical research and the work of ADEE at Biggin Hill which made the transition to RDF so relatively easy and effective. Without the foundation work on the command and control system, the late arrival of RDF to the defence armoury might well have been less effective and may not have tipped the delicate balance of the Battle of Britain in our favour. The next step would be the effective vectoring of fighters to intercept the incoming raiders and, as we will see, this too was to be developed at RAF Biggin Hill.

CHAPTER EIGHT

THE TIZARD COMMITTEE

The Biggin Hill Experiments

Since the end of WWI one subject had been at the top of the defence agenda, how to defend the United Kingdom from air attack and, in particular, London. Winston Churchill, Stanley Baldwin, Liddel-Hart and many others had offered the gravest warnings of the future of air power, the defences against which would mainly rest in early detection and effective destruction. Recognising that science could play a role in such matters a new committee was to be formed. In his instructive work, 'Most Secret War', Professor RV Jones, mentions a key warning from AP Rowe, the personal assistant to HE Wimperis, the Director of Scientific Research (DSR) at the Air Ministry. In 1934 he cautioned that:

> '…unless science evolved some new method of aiding our defences, we are likely to lose the next war if it started in the next ten years.'

As a result of discussions it was decided to form a new committee, the Committee for the Scientific Survey of Air Defence (CSSAD) and that Henry Tizard was to be its chairman. RV Jones also commented that:

'There is absolutely no doubt that Tizard was the best possible choice as Chairman. He had all the desirable experience, both as a scientist and as a serving officer; he had acute experience of armament development; he had inherent faith in technology; and he was an understanding and skilful chairman. The difficulties with Lindemann apart, he was fortunate in his opportunity. He had on the one side a considerable potential of scientific knowledge and enthusiasm to draw upon, both in Government Research Establishments and in the Universities; and on the other side he had a cadre of serving officers in the Royal Air Force who realised that in the difficult problem of air defence their service was 'up against it' and who were therefore particularly ready to try out any device that might offer promise. As an ultimate stroke of good fortune, Watson Watt had produced, just as the Tizard Committee met for the first time on 28th January 1935, the idea that it might be possible to detect an aircraft by the energy that is reflected from a radio transmitter on the ground.'

Henry Tizard (later Sir) is not a name that is well known, and yet he added a huge amount to science, particularly during WW1 and WW2. He grew up in Gillingham, Kent, and was expected to follow his Navy Captain father into a career at sea. However a freak accident with a fly which entered his left eye, causing him to close it, exposed a blind spot in his right eye. Although not thought to be permanent it was enough to see him concentrate more on his academic work than thinking of going to sea. With a sharp mind he grasped mathematics and won a scholarship to Westminster School and from there was accepted for Oxford. In 1905 he gained a First in Mathematical Moderations and then went on to study chemistry, achieving a First in 1908. At the time Germany was the Mecca for scientists and in September Tizard set off for Berlin, where he was to meet Frederick Lindemann (later Lord Cherwell) who, some thirty years later, was to become Churchill's chief scientific advisor.

At the outbreak of WW1 Tizard was in Australia with the British Association, but on returning to the motherland, in October 1914, was quick to enlist. Joining the Royal Garrison Artillery he reported to Clarence Barracks in Portsmouth, where he soon became responsible for the training of local territorials in the use of the anti-aircraft gun. His analysis of the capabilities of the weapon at hand was not encouraging; he said, 'One might possibly have hit a low flying Zeppelin with it, but the chance of hitting an aeroplane was negligible.'

Sir Henry Tizard 1885-1959

In 1915 he was asked by a colleague, Dr Robert Bourdillon, if he would transfer to the Royal Flying Corps (RFC) at the Central Flying School at Upavon, on the edge of Salisbury Plain. On arrival he immediately began work on the improvement of the very rudimentary bomb sites of the time but came to a point where his not being a pilot was limiting. He asked to be trained but the War Office would not release the instructor time necessary for someone who wasn't going on active service, but they did say he could make use of instructor time when the weather was too bad for the regular students to fly. Tizard's attitude was typical of his character; he said it would get the difficulties out of way first. He took a couple of half hour lessons a week and flew his first solo in less than three hours. He went on to pass his final test in just over thirty hours and qualified for his 'wings' later in the year. Flying not only opened up great opportunities for him to understand the difficulties experienced by pilots at the front, but also helped speed up his research. It also offered him greater mobility and he often flew to Farnborough to meet with Lindemann and the other leading lights. When the Aeroplane Experimental Unit (later to be dubbed the Aeroplane and Armament Experimental Unit) moved to Martlesham Heath, in 1917, Tizard was among the first to land.

Essentially, what Tizard was able to bring to development project was a systematic, scientific approach which moved projects forward logically and quickly. For instance, he had observed that much test flying was undertaken by experienced pilots back (on rest) from the front. However their approach to test flying was simply to fly the wings off new models (sometimes literally) and give scant formal feedback. Tizard introduced a system of test flying which, up to recently, was still the basic formula for testing and evaluating aircraft. He approached all problems in this manner with clear progress and sometimes far reaching results; for instance the introduction of anti-knocking additive (TEL - Tetra-Ethyl Lead) into aviation fuel which allowed the use of higher compression ratios, offering more power and economy, crucial for engines like the Merlin to provide the performance required.

The committee was as a direct result of the warning given by AP Rowe who, as mentioned earlier, was the personal assistant to HE Wimperis, the Director of Scientific Research (DSR) at the Air Ministry. Harry Wimperis was a scientist and had worked during WWI on a bomb sight that took into account the action of the wind on a bomb as it fell, eventually developing it into the 'Drift Sight' which allowed the approach to the target from any direction. He continued this work with the Royal Naval Air Service, making the transition to the Royal Air Force when the services were consolidated, and then on to an Air Ministry post where he eventually became the DSR. Albert Rowe was his personal assistant and, following the warning he had issued to Wimperis regarding the dangers of air power, he followed him on to the new Tizard Committee as secretary. Professor Patrick Blacket FRS, had joined the Navy as a Cadet in 1914 and had served at both the Battle of the Falkland Islands and at Jutland. He was commissioned as a Lieutenant before the end of the war when he resigned to study under Rutherford at Cambridge and is probably best known for his work on Cloud Chambers. Professor Archibald Hill, a renowned physiologist, was to become the fifth member of the committee which was to meet for the first time on Monday 28 January 1935. Its brief was simple but vital:

> 'To consider how far recent advances in scientific and technical knowledge can be used to strengthen the present methods of defence against hostile aircraft'.

It was scientific rigor which Tizard brought to the new committee, together with a brilliant mind and a complete understanding of modern aerial warfare as it was unfolding. He predicted that the accepted approach speed of attacking bombers would increase exponentially from the accepted 80 nautical mph (knots) (148 km/h) to in excess of 250 knots (460 km/h) within a few years, and that if the German Air Force (for instance) was beaten back in daylight attacks they would switch to night time bombing, against which Britain was, essentially, defenceless. What was needed was a system of early warning to alert the defenders and, better, a means of giving them a predicted course and a calculated vector (bearing) to intercept the intruders. In WWI this had only been achieved by flying standing patrols, essentially stooging around looking for the enemy, which was wasteful of fuel, wearing on aircraft, and fatiguing of pilots.

It was a matter that was keenly felt at ADEE Biggin Hill and work had proceeded on the disc systems, the sound mirrors, sound locators and improvements in optical equipment. Much of the information gained at ADEE was to be considered by the Tizard Committee but in the early days of its existence a wide spectrum of defence measure were tabled. For instance; numerous methods of deploying a steel wire barrage suspended from balloons, hung between enormous towers or hauled aloft by tethered or remotely operated helicopters; a scheme to cover the Thames with 'dark powder' so as to confuse visual navigation at night and the apparent reason why Danson Park Lake in Welling, Kent, was drained for the duration of the war, so it couldn't be used as a navigation aid - setting aside the existence of the huge and distinctive curve of the Thames around the Isle of Dogs just a couple of miles to the north-west which clearly identified London and the docks. Other serious suggestions included areas of floodlighting of massive candlepower to silhouette enemy aircraft against the cloud cover; a scheme to drop hundreds of small bomblets from aircraft flying higher than the enemy - apparently ignoring the prospect of the countryside being littered with unexploded live ordnance; wire bolas that would be loaded into anti-aircraft shells to entangle aircraft (and also probably wreak untold damage on falling at high speed to earth) and the detonation of the explosive content of bombs in situ by a beam of electromagnetic radiation.

However, amongst the plethora of new and sometimes fantastic schemes there came the development of solid defence science and here, once more, Biggin Hill was to be front and centre. Tizard's CSSAD was to be quick to recognise the potential of RDF and, once (hopefully) having positively located an inbound enemy formation, to be able to scramble fighters and to vector them towards their target. The complex equation involved in calculating the best interception course was to fall fairly on the officer commanding RAF Biggin Hill and the pilots of No. 32 Squadron.

The process of dealing with information identifying a positive contact was broadly the same whether it had been made by acoustic means or, eventually, by RDF. Both systems were outward looking from the coast and beyond that the plotting of the progress of the raiders would become the business of the Observer Corps (OC), which is all too often forgotten. Having been alerted to the approach of a raid and its position, constitution, strength and course, determined by the Mk I human eyeball, information would be fed to the filter room to be plotted on a large map table. Also marked on the table would be the positions of the fighter stations and disposition displays on the wall would show the state of readiness of squadrons at those stations – the classic scene which would become so familiar in pictures and film clips from the central operations room at RAF Uxbridge.

The next stage in the process was to identify the nearest available fighter squadrons and order them to scramble. But then come the problem of how they were to be vectored (given an altitude to attain - based on the observations of the OC via the Micklethwait or Post Instrument) and magnetic compass heading to fly to achieve an interception. However apparently simple the problem, the conundrum was how to calculate where the enemy would be by the time the fighters had climbed to altitude and closed on them. For example, a raid is detected over the Channel, its strength and composition evaluated by the OC with subsequent observations confirming landfall over Dover and on course for the London Docks on a heading of 295 degrees (m). Fighters scrambled from Biggin Hill and, perhaps,, Manston, need entirely different headings to intercept the enemy who, ten minutes after crossing the coast, will be in the area of Rochester and Gravesend. Given that it took a Hurricane or Spitfire about seven minutes of hard climbing to reach 20,000ft, a fair estimate from scramble to an attacking altitude would be ten to twelve minutes. In that time, as has been demonstrated, the target would have moved, and the art of successful interception was to have the defending fighters climbing towards the point in the sky close to, or ideally in front of, the enemy when they arrived. A similar equation had to be calculated if the fighters were already airborne and were re-vectored to a target. In 1936 this became a key issue for the newly formed Fighter Command, resulting in the Biggin Hill Experiments.

Leading up to this, in 1923, the Steel-Bartholomew Committee recommended the creation of the Air Defence of Great Britain (ADGB) command. This, in turn, had history going back to the end of WW1 and the deliberations of the Committee of Imperial Defence. There it had been agreed that it was unlikely the United Kingdom would be drawn into another major conflict for at least ten years. This became a tool of the committee and was known, quite simply, as the ten year rule. Creating such rule is now viewed, with the benefit of hindsight, as a hobbling restriction imposed upon the Committee which, if nothing else, tended to engender an atmosphere of complacency. The early focus was on the Navy and the discussion as to whether, having essentially only fought few classic naval engagements in

WWI, Jutland and the Battle of the Falkland Islands being two of the principal examples, the existing makeup of the Navy was appropriate. The discussion surrounded the question of whether in fact there was still a necessity for the fleet based on the capital ship (of which the UK had about sixty – and nearly three thousand other vessels), or if a step up in technology and a downsizing to submarines and aircraft would be a more appropriate use of scant funds; in the end the battleship won.

On a geopolitical scale, the chief threat to Imperial interests was considered to be in the Far East, Europe having been bled dreadfully during the preceding four year conflict. Plans were therefore considered for the bolstering of bases like Singapore to ensure the fleet could be effective if required to fight in that theatre. Interestingly enough, in Europe, it was recognised that France was probably the most significant potential, if unlikely, aggressor; based only on the not insignificant facts that, following the Great War and Treaty of Versailles, Germany was militarily out of the picture, Italy was in chaos, as was Russia, and Belgium was devastated. Therefore France which, despite the huge losses it suffered in the war, still had a massive army, a significant air force of some three hundred bombers, three hundred fighters, army co-operation squadrons and a fair number of aircraft within its colonial organisation; all of which were highly mobile and could be brought to bear within days. Their navy, however, had diminished and did not offer a significant threat.

The United Kingdom had ended the war with a similarly large, fully trained army which was quickly demobilised to a relatively low level, but retaining the bulk of the trained and experienced men as reservists. The Royal Air Force came into existence in April 1918 and had literally thousands of aircraft and trained pilots on strength at the armistice, but again the demobilisation had been quick and the aircraft reduced dramatically in number, with only a fraction kept active or placed in storage. Only the Navy seemed to come out of the post war reductions in some kind of fighting order. The Chief of the Air Staff, Air Chief Marshal Trenchard, argued that such had been the development and effect of air power during the war that rather than be subordinate to the other more senior services, the air force should be expanded and become the first fighting arm for the defence of the

UK. However, conventional naval power still dominated the debate, but he was at least able to achieve a break away from the War Office, and the Air Ministry was formed. This, for our immediate purposes, explains why at Biggin Hill the active aerodrome was always so distinctly separated from the War Office site in South Camp. But in practical terms, the Air Ministry was still subordinate to the needs of the army and navy and had no direct responsibility in developing air defence.

Throughout the early twenties the rather unsatisfactory arrangements of committees and sub-committees plodded forward. Finally, at the behest of Trenchard, as Chairman of a Joint Services Committee, Air Commodore JM Steel from the Air Ministry and Colonel WH Bartholomew from the War Office were tasked with setting up yet another sub-committee to resolve the question of the Defence of the United Kingdom. A central problem was that there were many overlaps in disciplines as the air force developed. Anti-aircraft guns and searchlights, for instance, were a key part of defence, but the Air Ministry had no experience of them, and the War Office were reluctance to give them up. Thus was created the Air Defence of Great Britain command with Air Marshal Sir John Salmond as the first Air Officer Commanding in Chief (AOC in C) with the Headquarters at Hillingdon House, Uxbridge. In June, 1935, the government approved the creation of a Metropolitan Air Force of 120 Squadrons (85 bomber squadrons and 35 fighters) and the following year the air fighting arm was reorganised into the three commands, Fighter Command, Bomber Command and Coastal Command. Fighter Command came into being on 1 May 1936, with Air Chief Marshal Sir Hugh Dowding as AOC in C.

No. 32 Squadron Gloster Gauntlets in formation over Biggin Hill.

Via Bob Ogley - Froglets Publications

No. 32 Squadron Gauntlets on the ground at Biggin Hill.
Below a scramble, probably staged for an open day, usually Empire Day.

No. 32 Squadron Gauntlets at Biggin Hill circa 1937.
Below: Another scramble, probably for the benefit of
the press or at another Empire open day.

No. 32 Squadron Gauntlets of 'B' Flight, March 1937. Soon after this picture was taken, 'B' Flight No. 32 Squadron became the nucleus of No. 79 Squadron when it was reformed on March 22.

Interior of the small Watch Office (the early equivalent of a Control Tower) at Biggin Hill, sited to the east of Station Headquarters and the first Operations Room. (Ced Verdon)

CHAPTER NINE

THE BIGGIN HILL EXPERIMENTS

How to Intercept the Enemy When Detected

Henry Tizard, as Chairman of the CSSAD, was keeping a very active watching brief on both acoustic detection and RDF to provide warning of an approaching threat. As discussed earlier, once a plot was firmed up, the critical question was how to vector fighters on to it efficiently. Things had moved on significantly from WWI, not least in the speeds expected by enemy bombers, so it simply wasn't practical to have squadrons on standing patrols, hoping to sight the enemy and attack. To press the question of interception Tizard attended a meeting at the Air Ministry on 13th July 1936, to discuss this very matter. Unfortunately parts of pages of the minutes are missing, but sufficient remains to observe the commencement of the process.

Tizard explained that his committee was hopeful that RDF would be able to provide warning of approaching formations, and that the best results to date had achieved this at 75 miles (120 km). Large scale tests were planned for the autumn and he outlined some tests and experiments which would help develop RDF. Also in process was an enlargement of the system of monitoring the progress of the raiders once they had crossed the coast (essentially RDF was outward looking from the coast, as were the sound mirrors). This would include an expansion of the Observer Corps and an increase in their training and improvement of equipment. However, in order to make the most efficient use of the tracking information available a series of experiments was proposed:

Experiment Number 1

'To determine the percentage of occasions on which interception could be expected on a clear day in clear weather when warning and the approximate position of the enemy is given ten minutes distance from the coast, and to obtain data as to the time that will elapse between receipt of the warning and interception taking place.'

Experiment Number 2 - (Here the original first sentence, which is reproduced here, had a typed substitution stuck over it).

Original text: 'To determine how close to a bomber, whose approximate position and course has been found by RDF, it is possible to direct a fighter by instructions from the ground.'

Substituted text: 'This information is required to determine what range will be required of an RDF set for installation in a fighter aircraft for use at night or in poor visibility, and also as an aid to determining the practicability of using mobile wire barrages against aircraft in cloud.'

The text then continues with the last part of the original paragraph which reads, 'This experiment should be carried out in clear weather, but fighters would be required to maintain their predetermined course when they sight the bombers and note how close it brought them to the bombers.'

Experiment Number 3

'Preliminary investigations had shown that the lights of London illuminating a cloud layer had enabled a Heyford bomber flying at 6,000ft to pick up the silhouette of another Heyford flying at 500ft above the cloud layer when 1½ miles away. It was now proposed to install a number of flood lights in some chosen locality which would produce a greater intensity of illumination than the London lights, and reports of skilled night pilots were required showing:-

(i) the possibility of this method for locating aircraft flying above the cloud at night;

(ii) what was the dazzling effect of the floodlights on the bombers.'

The thinking behind this system (Experiment No. 3) is probably best illustrated by some of the RAF film of the bombing of Germany in WW2. Some unique clips show bombers passing under one another, clearly silhouetted against under-lit smoke or cloud. The theory was that high flying fighters could take advantage of this and swoop down on the enemy. A small section of the report is missing here but on the next page Tizard explains that he would like to see the experiments started in August or September, and that he would be prepared to make himself available for advice for those two months.

For the first two experiments, which are of more immediate interest to us, it was agreed that aircraft and crews would have to be provided from operational units, even at the expense of pre-arranged training schedules, such was the urgency attached to the experiments. In any event, experienced pilots would be required who were already used to working with a sector controller. To assimilate war conditions as much as possible, it was agreed that bomber aircraft would be represented by flights of aircraft, whilst fighters could either be flights or a squadron. It was desirable for the 'enemy' to operate from a position of about 70-80 miles out to sea and the thought was that Avro Ansons would be the best choice, but it was pointed out that 'flights' of Ansons would probably not be available. It was therefore agreed that Hawker Hinds would be the 'enemy' as they could operate at least 20 miles off the coast, however it would be necessary for them to give their first positions as being 60 or so miles further out and to actually commence their approach after a suitable time lapse.

Control of the experiments was to be delegated to an experienced sector commander and the operations room selected should be able to maintain direct radio contact with the bombers to receive positional reports from the bombers, which could then be passed on to the fighters. On the face of it this may appear to be cheating, the bombers giving their positions and being tracked by the use of radio direction finding, but the experiments were to improve the quality of interception and would, in the future, depend upon the successful development of RDF and the expansion and training of the Observer Corps. As to the choice of the locations for the tests, the Deputy

Chief of the Air Staff emphasised that the choice of sector commander to control the experiments was of great importance and that he should not be selected merely because his sector was the most suitable. Henry Tizard was to be put in touch with him to advise on the exact nature of the experiments to be carried out.

Following this, on 14 July, Air Commodore WS Douglas, serving at the Air Ministry as Director of Staff Duties (DSD), wrote to Air Marshal PB Joubert de la Ferte at Headquarters No. 11 Group, Fighter Command, on behalf of the Deputy Chief of the Air Staff, apprising him of the requirements outlined in the previous day's meeting. He wrote that Mr Tizard had asked if a flight of fighters (either Gauntlets or Furies); a flight of bombers whose speed is not more than 30 or 40 mph less than the fighters, proposing the use of a flight of Hinds; and a sector control room at a station which had efficient D/F (Direction Finding) apparatus. Douglas went on to write that he had been informed by the Director of Signals that Biggin Hill and Hornchurch had D/F with a range of about 40 miles; North Weald and Duxford had a range of 60 miles and Northolt had 70 miles. He continued by reporting that Mr Tizard wanted to be able to monitor the position of the fighter flight as accurately as possible in the air as far as the coast and concluded that this would exclude Biggin Hill, but that Hornchurch would fit the bill as it was nearer the coast. He ruled out Northolt as they were apparently busy with other experimental work but considered either North Weald or Duxford as possibilities.

The DSD then went on to discuss the personality of the Sector Commander who would be needed to directly assist Tizard in his work, remarking that the right person would need to be 'bright and intelligent with practical experience', and suggested Lee (Wing Commander AS Lee) at Hornchurch but did draw attention to the limited D/F range of the equipment there. Air Commodore Douglas summed up the first part of his communication by asking Air Marshal Joubert to take the above considerations into account and make suggestions.

On 17 July Joubert replied, stating unequivocally that Biggin Hill would be the most suitable Sector Station from which these experiments should be carried out. He also wrote a glowing recommendation for the Station

Sir Philip Sassoon, Under-Secretary of State for Air (1931-1937) in a flying suit.
Right is Wing Commander EO Grenfell, Officer Commanding RAF Biggin Hill.
Behind them is one of the Pilots' Ready Rooms (which still exists) and to the left
is the end of the huge hangar which once stood on the present day site of St
George's Memorial Chapel. (Bob Ogley - Froglets Publications)

Commander, Wing Commander EO Grenfell, stating that he had already carried out a considerable number of interception experiments of a very similar nature during the preceding twelve months. He continued, regarding the flying aspect, that No. 32 Squadron could produce personnel with a good standard of R/T (radio telephony) knowledge and had pilots already well experienced in D/F, proposing that two flights be used from the Squadron, one in August and one in September. He further comments that No. 32 Sqn was in the process of re-arming from Bristol Bulldogs to Gloster Gauntlets, of which five were already on the squadron strength. He also makes a couple of very strong points, the first that high priority had to be given to the issue of new R/T controls for the Gauntlets by the Director of Signals and, for continuity, the Director of Personnel should ensure that the Squadron pilots would remain unchanged for the duration.

Commenting on the perceived lack of range of the D/F equipment at Biggin Hill, Joubert wrote that the ranges previously quoted were subject to the heights at which the aircraft would be required to fly. Presumably the altitudes in prospect being 6,000ft (1,000 m) and above would effectively increase the range. However another development at Biggin Hill may well have been associated with these experiments.

At about the same time as the Biggin Hill experiments were beginning, a local lad, Frank Goodridge, observed two things as, like many small boys, he watched the activities at the aerodrome with keen interest. First was the very obvious increase of flying activity towards the end of the summer in 1935, and second was the rapid construction of a wood and corrugated iron building between the aerodrome and his village, Downe. He described it as being on stilts and had large shutters on the sides which could be opened. Telephone wires led away from the building to the aerodrome and there were regular changes of personnel at this peculiar construction (see illustration). It is entirely possible that this new building, which was set on ground at the same elevation as the aerodrome and to the north-east, diametrically opposite the position of the Ops Room, was for improved D/F. If indeed this was the purpose of this construction its position may have been dictated to take it away from possible interference from transmissions associated with the radio aerials at the Ops Room, which was situated 1¼ miles (2 km) away on the western side of Main Road, between the Officers' Mess and Saltbox Hill.

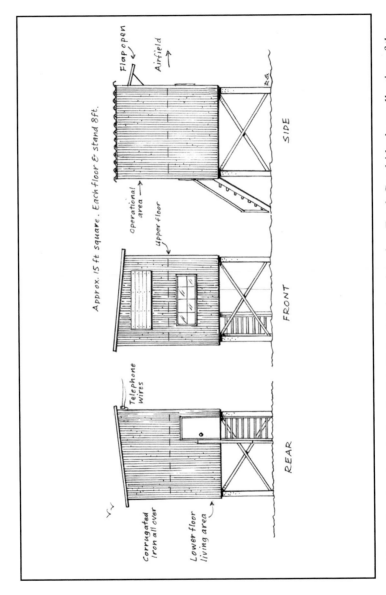

This is a drawing done by local artist, Richard Geiger, based on Frank Goodridge's recollection of the building which appeared near Downe at about the same time as the Biggin Hill Experiments.

Continuing to expand the operation to get the experiments underway, on 20 July Air Cdre Douglas wrote to Wg Cdr AW Mylne at Headquarters, Bomber Command at Uxbridge, at the request of the Deputy Chief of the Air Staff (DCAS). He mentioned the proposed Tizard experiments and detailed their requirements as being:

A Flight of Fighters (either Gauntlets or Furies)

A Flight of 3 Bombers whose speed is not more than 30 or 40 mph less than the fighter (proposing the use of a flight of Hawker Hinds).
A sector operations room at a station which has an efficient D/F apparatus for determining the position of fighter aircraft.

He went on to report that he had taken up the question of the fighters and sector operations room with Air Officer Commanding No. 11 (Fighter) Group, but asked if a flight of Hinds could be made available, whilst recognising that many squadrons will be on leave during August, but pressing the point that once committed, the same flight should be used throughout the experiments. He closed by asking which squadron or squadrons could provide the flight, and for an officer to be nominated as a point of contact for Henry Tizard; lastly informing Mylne that Joubert at 11 Group had already suggested Biggin Hill for the Ops Room, the Sector Commander and for No. 32 Squadron to provide fighters so that he could make the best choice of bombers to cover that area.

This communication seems to have led to a telephone conversation which was mentioned in a follow up communication dated 25 July. In this Mylne confirms that Bomber Command could supply a flight of Hinds from various sources and details:

Period: 1 – 12 August from No. 57 (B) Sqn Upper Heyford

Period: 13 – 31 August from No. 49 (B) Sqn Worthy Down

Period: 1 – 30 September from RAF Station Abingdon

Mylne pointed out that the only doubtful period was the second one in August because No. 49 Sqn was a new one-flight 'throw-off' squadron and would only have been at its new Station, Worthy Down, for a couple of days. To cover this exigency Douglas wrote to AOC No. 22 (Army Co-operation) Group, RAF, South Farnborough on 27 July, asking for a Flight of Hinds because of the uncertainty surrounding No. 49 Sqn's move and availability (and probably experience). He also commented that Wg Cdr EO Grenfell at Biggin Hill was in charge of the experiments and that he had been authorised to communicate direct with those involved in flying arrangements.

In retrospect it seems anomalous that only on 27 July does Air Cdre Douglas write to the Air Officer Commanding in Chief (AOC in C) Fighter Command, Sir Hugh CT Dowding (see Appendix 3 for the full text), announcing that it has been recommended that Interception Experiments should take place between August and September, 1936, at the instigation of and under the control of the Committee for the Scientific Survey of Air Defence (the Tizard Committee). Further that No. 32 Squadron at Biggin Hill was designated for the Fighter role; a series of Bomber Squadrons were listed to take part for various periods, and Wg Cdr EO Grenfell (Officer Commanding RAF Biggin Hill) was to be both Sector Controller and in charge of the experiments; he was also to report directly to Henry Tizard

The next day Dowding replied from Bentley Priory, Stanmore, stating that the instructions had been passed to Air Officer Commanding (AOC) No. 11 (Fighter) Group, in which Biggin Hill fell, and that it was agreed that Wg Cdr EO Grenfell would be placed in charge. Dowding also pointed out that as, '*...no information as to the nature of the experiments which are to be undertaken had been given and, therefore, according to the procedure proposed, Wing Commander Grenfell and Mr Tizard would be in complete control not only of the details but also of the experiments as a whole*'.

However the AOC in C was not going to let things rest there and on 7 August a conference was called at Bentley Priory to discuss Special Interception Exercises at Biggin Hill. Present were:

Air Marshal Sir Hugh CT Dowding
Mr HT Tizard
Mr HE Wimperis
Air Commodore JHS Tyssen
Wing Commander EO Grenfell
Air Commodore AD Cunningham
Mr AP Rowe

Dowding was, of course, the AOC in C of the relatively new Fighter Command, Tizard was Chairman of the CSSAD, HE Wimperis was Director of Scientic Research at the Air Ministry and a member of Tizard's committee, Air Commodore Tyssen was Senior Air Staff Officer (SASO) at No. 11 Group, Wing Commander Grenfell was OC RAF Biggin Hill, Air Commodore AD Cunningham was SASO to Dowding, and AP Rowe was both personal assistant to HE Wimperis at the Air Ministry and also Secretary to the Tizard Committee.

Dowding opened the meeting by referring to the points which had led up to it, stating that he had '... *received a letter from the Air Ministry, saying that the Committee of (sic) Scientific Survey of Air Defence had recommended that certain experiments should be carried out in connection with the problems of interception of bomber aircraft by fighters'*. The cardinal points from the correspondence with the Air Ministry were read out and a discussion ensued, during which Henry Tizard said he '... emphatically disclaimed any desire to be in executive control of the experiments and it was agreed that there was no reason to interfere with the normal chain of command, provided that direct touch between Wg Cdr Grenfell and Mr Tizard was constantly maintained.'

The C in C read from the document forwarded to him by the Air Ministry and is recorded as saying, *'The Air Ministry wants to determine the probable percentage of interceptions. How many runs would you require to strike a percentage? Would you be content with 20 for instance?'* Here Tizard demonstrated his scientific pragmatism, replying, *'I am afraid the answer to that would only be known after 20 have been done. It would depend, for instance, upon the extent to which these 20 had covered various types of weather.'* To which Dowding replied, *'We have for the moment only been given 2 months for uninterrupted work on these experiments. Do you consider that this will be sufficient?'* Tizard's reply was again pragmatic, *'I think 2 months is far too short. I have a feeling that once these experiments have been started and you begin to get results, everyone will be convinced that the experiments must go on. I am prepared to say, here and now, that 2 months is much too short. If you want a guess I will give you one. I should say a year.'*

Dowding accepted Tizard's statement and added that the Air Ministry would have to give up a flight of bombers and a number of fighters for that time and commented that the sooner they were apprised of the situation the better. Tizard re-enforced his argument by saying that at the end of two months Dowding and the Air Ministry will be convinced that this type of experiment should be continued. As a good tactician Dowding was already thinking ahead and said that unless the Ministry knew that the experiments were likely to continue they would likely post away key personnel at the end of two months.

The subject of the conditions for the experiments must have been raised as Air Commodore Tyssen questioned whether by *'normal daylight'* Tizard meant, *'... any weather in which the enemy may reasonably be supposed to attack'*. Tizard agreed and Dowding added that the bombers had to give their position every five minutes and therefore had to be able to see the ground. Of course this was for the sake of the experiments, under wartime conditions it would be up to the Observer Corps to report the position of formations as they tracked across the countryside. Tizard said that the position of the bombers could also be determined by the use of D/F equipment, but the accuracy of this kind of plot would not be known until after the experiments had time to run.

Here we are seeing some of the developments at Biggin Hill coming together; the early expansion of the use of radio in aircraft (first driven by Major Dowding at Brooklands and eventually maturing at the RAF Wireless Experimental Establishment) and D/F - Direction Finding - which, as has been illustrated earlier, was honed at Biggin Hill. It is impossible to estimate how influential good radio communications were when faced with a determined enemy; air to ground/ground to air and air-to-air telephony would become vital for effective command and control, an aspect of aerial warfare which was not widely appreciated in the *Luftwaffe*, for instance. In *'Spitfire on my Tail'* (Independent Books), Ulrich Steinhilper revealed the difficulties, as officer in charge of the *Nachrichtenzug* (communications section) for his *Gruppe*, he experienced with his squadron CO, the redoubtable Adolph Galland. Pre-war the *Luftwaffe* was very hierarchical, dominated by the so-called 'Spaniards' - those that had flown in the Spanish Civil War, of which Galland was one. In time honoured tradition they tended rely on past experience and could not see that radio telephony would be vital in any future, fast evolving combat zone. The theory has been put forward that traditional pilots like Galland foresaw the possibility of their squadrons being controlled from the ground and the loss of the *Freijagd* (free hunt), individually led by them in true Teutonic style, being lost. Another theory is that because Legion Condor was operating clandestinely in Spain, they didn't want radio traffic in German monitored and therefore developed other means of communication such as wing signals.

In 1939, following an extensive exercise to test the air defences of Stuttgart, Steinhilper thought he and his team had done well in controlling the defending fighters and passing information to them on the positions of the enemy. At the debrief Steinhilper asked a question of *General* Sperrle regarding the performance of the reporting and direction from the ground. Before the General could comment Galland stepped up and said, *'Good Steinhilper, you have reminded me - you were talking too much* (Steinhilper had been explicitly told by the *Gruppe* Commander to operate the transmitter personally). *You were just bothering us all the time. And as I've always told you, it would be best to throw out all of these damned radios! We don't need them. We didn't need them in Spain and without them we could fly higher and faster!'* It was therefore something of a surprise when, in 1985, Steinhilper read an article by Galland in *Jagerblatt* (the newsletter of the German Fighter Pilots Association) entitled, *'45 Years ago – At the Channel'*. He wrote, *'Looking back at the Battle of Britain, there was no radio direct radio communication possible with the bombers, due to different frequencies. A situation almost unbelievable which, amongst others, had seri-*

ous consequences when rendezvous points were missed or escorts/bombers were a little late.' The shortfall in German communications is therefore clear, as are the reasons why; it was to be an important factor in the eventual defeat of the *Luftwaffe* in 1940'. (See further note at the end of this chapter).

In terms of D/F - Direction Finding, development work had been undertaken at Biggin Hill, resulting in the possibility of aircraft being guided by on-board D/F equipment in 1918, as previously described. As D/F was a vital part of normal pilot training (obtaining a QDM - a magnetic bearing to fly to return to base) most pilots were familiar with it. However, as we will see, the extensive use of the D/F facilities to run the Biggin Hill Experiments would be raised in terms of reducing training facilities for newer pilots.

At Bentley Priory the conference continued with discussion of the use of D/F to give a series of positions for the bombers and the accuracy that could be expected. Briefly, the system was designed to give pilots who are temporarily uncertain of their position (pilots never get lost!) a magnetic bearing, uncorrected for wind, to fly to reach base. To do this they make a series of test transmissions, e.g. days of the week, months of the year, etc. whilst the loop aerials of the D/F equipment are rotated to pick up the strongest signal, the reciprocal bearing of which is the heading for home. Cross referencing this with a bearing from another set D/F equipment, like that at Hornchurch, will also give a spot position and some idea of how far away from base the pilot was. For the purposes of the Experiments, repeating the call sign for the aircraft to get the necessary fix identified it as 'friend' or 'foe'. In time of war the position would be detected by RDF or acoustically as the enemy approached the coast and thereafter tracked by the Observer Corps, calling in their plots to their control rooms. This and other information would then filtered and sent to Fighter Command Operations who would, in turn, relay it back to Sector Operations Rooms.

However as all this was still in the developmental stage it was still quite crude, but the question of how to intercept the enemy once located and track established was the main question. Over and above this, the actual line of the coast came up as it seemed the RAF were less than keen on their Hawker

Hinds flying too far out to sea at any time but, realistically, the detection of a raid some miles off the coast had to be the base line from which to begin because of the theoretical limitations of the developing RDF and the established limits of acoustic detection. Tizard said that the boffins working on RDF could, on occasion, establish a plot some 75 miles (120 km) out and could also 'make a good guess' of the number of aircraft involved. Further it also seemed they could detect when aircraft broke away from a formation, but for the purposes of the Biggin Hill Experiments 'the actual position of the coast was irrelevant'. The 'coast' was therefore to be set at 40 miles (64 km) from Charing Cross (usually accepted as the centre of London) and drawn in as an arc on the plotting table.

On another practical point for the forthcoming trials, Henry Tizard suggested that when the fighters reached the point at which they should intercept the bombers they would ignite a smoke candle and the bomber crews, on seeing this, would fly towards the point at which the trail started and thus, presumably, be able to estimate the accuracy of the interception (although this would probably be observed from the ground). Tizard also mentioned that the experiments would take into account the manoeuvring of a mobile barrage (something being considered by his committee), possibly to be drawn across the track of the raiders, either lifted aloft by balloons or by remote controlled helicopters! Dowding seized on the question of smoke candles, asking what colours were available and how they would be fitted to Gloster Gauntlets, which had no bomb racks, also commenting that if they needed something new it would probably take Woolwich [Arsenal] about six months to produce it. It was also agreed that because the personnel to operate the D/F equipment would need a lot of training to be competent, they should be staffed at a level of plus 50% over strength to allow for consistency during absences.

The decisions reached at the conference were:

> That during the first fortnight of the experiments aircraft should operate below the clouds and that bombers should be able to see the ground and report their positions.

> That the Air Ministry should be requested not to move any of the personnel responsible for operating the D/F stations at Northolt, North Weald and Biggin Hill until

after the completion of the experiments.

That an expert navigator was essential and that if possible the officer at present working at Biggin Hill (Squadron Leader Dickens) should be left there. If this was not possible the Air Ministry must send another qualified navigational officer to Biggin Hill and he should remain there during the course of the experiments.

That standard red coloured flares would be used during the experiments.

That the question of fitting wing-tip flare brackets and battery switches to the Gauntlets should be taken up by Wg Cdr Grenfell on very high priority.
Henry Tizard also raised the question of the crews of the bomber aircraft and stated that these men should be experienced. It was especially necessary to have experienced observers who would be able to take down notes efficiently, synchronise watches, take compass bearings, actual bearings, changes of course etc., and notes on weather conditions which are always valuable.

That three observers should be kept at Biggin Hill until the termination of the experiments. Dickens (the specialist navigator) would be a substitute at any time. This would make four and would always leave one of the four in the formation who would be efficient.

That [Sqn Ldr] Dickens would go up from time to time with the formation in order to obtain data.

Lastly it was agreed that Wg Cdr Grenfell at Biggin Hill would be in overall charge and determine the flying schedule and reporting back direct to Fighter Command HQ, with Tyssen at 11 Group and Dowding as AOC in C copied in.

A special plotting table was designed and built at the Royal Aircraft Establishment (RAE) Farnborough which consisted of a horizontal board, painted black with blackboard paint, 6ft x 4ft with cut-outs for the position of the controller of the bombers and, opposite, a similar arrangement for the controller fighters (see illustrationat the end of the chapter). A skeleton map to a scale of ¾ inch to a mile was already painted onto the table, covering the area of operations (Kent) with a thin line for the actual coast and a few prominent towns denoted by capital letters and airfields with a capital letter ringed (so 'S' is Sheerness and 'E' ringed is Eastchurch, 'C' is Canterbury and 'M' ringed is Manston). A compass rose was painted near to the airfield and another around a point of reference marked 'R' from which the position of the bombers could be plotted in terms of bearing and distance. At the point of reference a ¼ inch diameter bolt projected upward from the board to a height of ½ inch to form a pivot around which a special ruler could be orientated. This rule was notched every ¾ of an inch to represent each mile and by placing the notch against the bolt and orientating the ruler for the correct angle corresponding to the course of the bombers, the distance and bearing could be plotted in coloured chalk. Painted in a prominent position was a height scale, against which the bomber plotter could mark the height at which the 'enemy' were judged to be flying.

Interestingly, for the purposes of the exercises the point of reference (R) on the plotting board is recorded as being arbitrary. This was because on the Ordnance Survey map (Sheet 12 - RAF Edition) which was used for the tracings for the skeleton map on the board, there was a compass rose in that position and it was decided it would be as good a place as any to use. Also attached were Type 'C' Chart-Board Protractors with their parallel motion and hinged arms. Having set the wind speed and direction on these instruments, the fighter plotter was able to plot tracks and determine ground speeds from courses and airspeeds given by the Sector Commander to the fighters. The number and positions of these instruments on the plotting board would depend upon the position occupied by the fighter plotter and upon the probable area covered by the fighters during operations. The raid plotted on the board for the illustration is shown as Number 85 which took place on 5 October 1936 and Wg Cdr Grenfell is recorded as the Sector Commander.

Initially quite complicated equations were calculated using four vectors but this proved to be time consuming and requiring expert skills. By Experiment Number 37 the term, 'Method of Equal Angles', was being mentioned which would greatly speed up the process. Referring to Figure 1 (which is a copy of the actual figure in the file) the method is transcribed as follows on the next page:

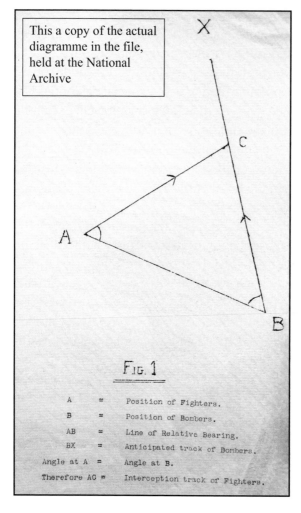

This a copy of the actual diagramme in the file, held at the National Archive

X

C

A

B

F₁G. 1

A	=	Position of Fighters.
B	=	Position of Bombers.
AB	=	Line of Relative Bearing.
BX	=	Anticipated track of Bombers.
Angle at A =		Angle at B.
Therefore AC =		Interception track of Fighters.

If A and B are the predicted positions of the Fighters and Bombers respectively at the time the interception course can be given to the Fighters, and BX is the track of the Bombers produced; join AB and consider this as the base of an Isosceles Triangle. From A draw AC so that the angle at A equals the angle at B. Then the side AC = the side BC. Now, if the Fighters at A travel along the track AC at a greater speed than the Bombers at B travel along the track BX, then the Fighters will cross the track of the Bombers at the point C before the Bombers themselves arrive at this point.

A note on the page qualifies the above and states:

It will be seen, then, that providing the Fighters have a superiority of speed over the Bombers, the application of the 'Principal of Equal Angles' will inevitably place the Fighters in a position ahead of the Bombers on the latter's track. The Fighters may then be stopped and instructed to circle and wait for the Bombers to come up to them.

Inevitably, given the input on the experiments by Henry Tizard himself, the method was christened the *'Tizzy Angle'*. The method proved to be highly effective with interceptions achieved in all experimental raids. Further, the complex calculations and the necessity for the precise use of the pantographs could be dispensed with, considerably lifting the work load from the navigation officer and controller. This was another of the crucial developments which took place at Biggin hill between the wars which were to profoundly affect the outcome of the Battle of Britain.

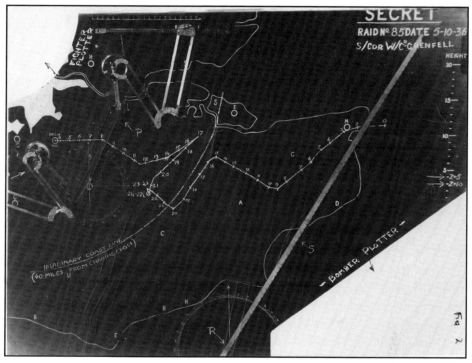

A skeleton map to a scale of ¾ inch to a mile was already painted onto the table, covering the area of operations (Kent) with a thin line for the actual coast and a few prominent towns denoted by capital letters and airfields with a capital letter ringed (so 'S' is Sheerness and 'E' ringed is Eastchurch, 'C' is Canterbury and 'M' ringed is Manston). A compass rose was painted near to the airfield and another around a point of reference marked 'R' from which the position of the bombers could be plotted in terms of bearing and distance. At the point of reference a ¼ inch diameter bolt projected upward from the board to a height of ½ inch to form a pivot around which a special ruler could be orientated. This rule was notched every ¾ of an inch to represent each mile and by placing the notch against the bolt and orientating the ruler for the correct angle corresponding to the course of the bombers, the distance and bearing could be plotted in coloured chalk. Painted in a prominent position was a height scale, against which the bomber plotter could mark the height at which the 'enemy' were judged to be flying.(Copied from the file in the National Archive)

Pilots of No. 32 Squadron are briefed prior to a flight, possibly in association with the Biggin Hill Experiments. In the top left hand corner can be seen the cupola on top of the roof of the Station HQ.

Note (1)

The Observer Corps moved to RAF Bentley Priory from its original location at RAF Uxbridge, along with Dowding and Fighter Command, during July 1936 and would remain at the Priory until it was stood down in December 1995. The Observer Corps was one of the cornerstones of Lord Dowding's air defence system and he said later in his despatch after the Battle of Britain:

'It is important to note that at this time they (the Observer Corps) constituted the whole means of tracking enemy raids once they had crossed the coastline. Their work throughout was quite invaluable. Without it the air-raid warning systems could not have been operated and inland interceptions would rarely have been made.'

As a result of their efforts during the Battle of Britain the Observer Corps was granted the title Royal by King George VI and became a uniformed volunteer branch of the RAF from April 1941 for the remainder of its existence. Throughout its service the Royal Observer Corps was commanded by an RAF Air Commodore, each of whom served a tour of between three or four years.

Note (2)

Adolf 'Dolfo' Galland did not fly fighters during the Spanish Civil War but specialised in ground attack. Although he and his colleagues may have been somewhat short sighted regarding communications before World War 2 he was to become a very significant figure in the *Luftwaffe*, finally becoming *General der Jagdflieger*. However, because of constant disagreements with Goering on fighter tactics, and in particular the use of the Me. 262, he was finally relieved of command and virtually placed under house arrest. However, after something of a mutiny amongst the high ranking *Luftwaffe* officer corps he was reinstated and allowed to form *Jagdverband 44 (JV 44)*. *Jagdverband* is really translated as a hunting association, rather than the more usual *Jagdgruppe (JG)* - fighter or hunter group, this was to distinguish it from the normal *Luftwaffe* organisation - Goering hadn't entirely forgiven Galland and his close associates for their 'impudence'. *Jagdverband 44*, also known as *Der Galland Zirkus* (Galland's Circus) operated from Munich (Riem) during the closing weeks of the war, using the Me. 262 which Galland had wanted to use as a fighter from its first concept. The fighters took part in aerial combats with the USAF in the very last days of the war and were disproportionally effective against the American bombers, probably proving that the earlier development of the Me. 262 as a front line fighter instead of Hitler and Goering's obsession with making a *Schnellbomber* (fast bomber) for revenge would have had a catastrophic effect on the bombing campaign by greatly increasing the losses taken by the Allies. Galland survived the war but his two brothers were killed, both pilots. He later became close friends with several distinguished Allied pilots; he died in February, 1996.

CHAPTER TEN

TO WAR

Biggin Hill Takes the Fight to Germany

In the introduction to this work it was made clear that the purpose of it was to bring forward many aspects of the history of RAF Biggin Hill which, to date, have not been explored in any great depth. Certainly the part played by Biggin Hill in the Battle of Britain has been told from many directions and, for the most part, fully explored. Following the great air battle Biggin Hill also played a key role in taking the fight back, beginning to probe the enemy strength in the occupied countries, providing air cover over the D-Day beaches, receiving many of the wounded as the campaign pushed through Europe, and finally welcoming back thousands of Prisoners of War, many of whom had be 'in the bag' since 1939. It is not proposed to completely circumnavigate this important time, but more to deal with a couple of aspects in detail, again using the few first-hand accounts still available, files in the National Archive, Operations Record Books and some other published accounts. So, forward to 1939 and the gathering clouds.

Number 601 Squadron was known as 'The Millionaires' and for the most part this was true. Many of the pilots were indeed multi-millionaires and counted amongst their number Max Aitken, son of Lord Beaverbrook, William Rhodes-Moorhouse whose family line went back to Cecil Rhodes and whose father had been the first airman to win a Victoria Cross in the air; Loel Guinness, Richard Dimitriadi, Henry Cavendish, Sir Archibald Hope and so on. They treated the Squadron like a gentleman's club and, for instance, were not only successful in getting American millionaire 'Billy' Fiske into the RAF, when his country was still neutral, but straight into their Squadron.

The Squadron was formed at Northolt on 14 October, 1925, by Lord Edward Grosvenor, arguably as an extension of White's Club in St James's, Westminster, also frequented by the wealthy; indeed many of the original pilots were already aviators and members of the Club. Pre-war No. 601 Squadron had enjoyed regular summer camps at Lympne, Kent, and were often found in the swimming pool and enjoying the plush surroundings of Port Lympne Mansion, near Hythe, Kent, owned by Sir Phillip Sassoon (also a millionaire), along with luminaries of the time such as Lawrence of Arabia. Sassoon was Under Secretary of State for Air twice, between 1924 and 1929, and again from 1931 to 1937 and was also Honorary Commanding Officer of the Squadron. He died in June 1939, of complications following a bout of influenza, but his influence on the tradition of the Squadron had been considerable and was to last.

Arriving at Biggin Hill the Squadron faced some interesting problems, one of which was the imminent application of petrol rationing and its projected effect on their ability to run their cars and powerful motor cycles. The then Squadron Leader, Brian Thynne, appointed Willie Rhodes-Moorhouse as Petrol Officer with instructions to make arrangements to stockpile fuel. Leaving Biggin Hill he motored towards Bromley and spotted a small garage on the left hand side of the road, just before the King's Arms pub at Leaves Green. Going inside he spoke to the owner, reminding him that the road to Westerham was to be closed or was already closed (versions of the story vary) and that through traffic was about to cease. The owner was, apparently, only too aware of his predicament and was amicable to an offer for the whole garage, made by Rhodes-Moorhouse, on the spot. With the deal agreed, Willie handed over a cheque and returned to Biggin Hill to report to Thynne that he'd solved the petrol problem. 'How much fuel do you have?' enquired the CO. 'Enough to last the war', replied Willie. He went on to explain what he'd done but confirmed that in fact there probably wasn't enough fuel to last out the war, however short people thought it would be. Calling upon Loel Guinness, Rhodes-Moorhouse asked if he remembered correctly that Guinness was a director of a subsidiary of the Shell oil company. Guinness admitted he didn't remember but phoned his secretary to confirm Willie's recollection. Indeed he was, and within a couple of days the tanks were topped off with fuel - problem solved - Rhodes-Moorhouse (and 601) style.

Pilots from No. 601 Squadron at Biggin Hill. Second from the left is Roger Bushell who was later shot down when flying with No. 92 Sqn, and became a prisoner of war. An inveterate escaper he was finally sent to *Stalagluft 3*, Zagan in Poland where he became 'Big X', organising the 'Great Escape'. However, he and forty-nine other escapees were to pay for their audacity with their lives. Bushell was shot by the Gestapo and left to die in a ditch. He was posthumously awarded a 'Mentioned in Dispatches'.

The small garage that was bought by Willie Rhodes-Moorhouse at Leaves Green, near the aerodrome. It is now a car sales site although the original garage facility underneath is still in use and the original wall on the left can still be seen. Below: Another view in the winter snow, showing the house next to the garage which was once owned by the Kray brothers. (Edward Williams)

With the declaration of war, a note was recorded in the HQ Operations Record Book (Form 504) which simply read:

Biggin Hill 3.9.39 11:00

The outbreak of war found a station headquarters, RAF Station Biggin hill, under the command of Wing Commander R Grice. The operational units on the station consisted of Nos. 32, 79, and 601 fighter squadrons. Nos. 32 and 79 squadrons were equipped with Hurricanes and 601 Squadron with Blenheim aircraft. Owing to the precautionary arrangements carried out during the emergency and mobilising periods, the station was in a high state of war preparedness. All AA defences were permanently manned and all aircraft dispersed.

The accommodation for airmen was strained to the utmost, but was eased by the use of new barrack blocks in course of construction, some of which were partially finished. It was necessary to accommodate 74 privates of the Queen's own Royal West Kent Regiment, attached for ground defence and guard duties, in the School of Anti-Aircraft Defence.

The question of airmen's messing accommodation was acute, but was relieved by using the two cooking trails allotted for satellite aerodromes, one being allotted to No. 79 Squadron at dispersal point, and the other to 601 squadron, in South Camp, where part of a hangar was used as an airmen's dining hall.

Two sections of the 90th Regt AA guns took up positions around the aerodrome at TATSFIELD and CUDHAM respectively.

The two Intelligence Officers F/Lt. Wendt and P/O Dennis were alerted the duties of cypher officers in addition to their own duties. P/O John Speyer reported for intelligence duties. The following officers had already reported for duty to take up war appointments on the dates shown against their names.

Patrols were soon being flown but it wasn't until 28 November that 601 Squadron was to take part in the first offensive operation flown by Fighter Command. German seaplanes had been operating out of the Frisian Islands, laying mines on the approaches to the eastern ports like Hull and Felixstowe, and regularly making visits to the Thames Estuary. No 25 Squadron had set off with a brief to attack the seaplane bases on 26 November but had turned back because of bad weather. On the 27 November six Blenheims from 601 were ordered to RAF Northolt without their gunners or navigators, three from 'A' Flight led by F/Lt Peacock and three from 'B' Flight led by F/Lt Aitken. Arriving at Northolt they were assigned navigators and gunners from Coastal Command – the logic being that they had more experience of flying marine operations. In the briefing room the Station CO, Wing Commander Augustus Orlebar, former chief of the successful British Schneider Trophy race team, bade the visitors welcome, and then said, 'Congratulations gentlemen, you're all very lucky, you are about to go to Germany!'

By later standards those present recorded that the Ops Brief was minimal and the planning, at best, was poor. Although a substantial part of the operation was to be over sea they were not, apparently, issued with dinghies or even life jackets. The pilots knew their target was the island of Borkum, about 150 miles (240 km) west of Hamburg, and the direct route would be 350-400 miles (560- 650 km). The combat range of their aircraft was in the order of 1000 miles (1600 km), depending greatly on wind and throttle settings for attack and aerial combat, which was a little close for comfort. Max Aitken suggested that the group should take off earlier than planned and land at Bircham Newton to top off their tanks and make their departure point closer to the target. This was accepted and the group had lunch in the mess, prior to departure. When one of the resident pilots heard their target was in Germany he apparently took some of them to a hangar to see a Whitley bomber. It was peppered with holes and had one huge gash in it through which anyone could easily climb. 'It used to be mine,' he said casually, 'but the flak got it; have a good trip.' The exchange of glances amongst the Blenheim boys can easily be imagined. Following this sobering visit they crewed up and began their pre-flight checks for a 14:15 start.

Flying over the North Sea the weather began to deteriorate and first thoughts were that the attack would have to be called off. Rain began to speckle the cockpits and then became heavier as the aircraft grouped up tighter to maintain visual contact. Close to the decision to break and run for home the aircraft burst out of the squally cloud within sight of the base, taking the German defences completely by surprise. Making several passes they machine gunned the seaplanes on the slipways and the hangars then broke off and formed up for the return flight, by which time the light was fading. Navigating by dead reckoning and avoiding burst of anti-aircraft fire from 'friendlies' they made landfall, steeply changing course to miss the Harwich barrage balloons. Having flown back out of the squalls over the North Sea the visibility was good and they soon spotted an illuminated runway (at Debden) where night flying training was taking place. Without further ado, or for that matter the courtesy of a request to land (none of the RT equipment seemed to be working), they entered the circuit and to the complete surprise of the duty controller 12 Blenheims streamed in, line astern, to be marshalled into various dispersals by the equally bemused ground crews.

There followed inspections of the aircraft and much back slapping and hand shaking, with the inevitable exchanges of experience in their first operational contact. The following morning the 601 Blenheims flew back to Biggin Hill, having been part of the first penetration of German airspace by Fighter Command. It also brought No. 601 Squadron its first decoration when F/Lt Michael Peacock was awarded the Distinguished Flying Cross. Max Aitken was mentioned in dispatches and Biggin Hill was once again on the map.

The international Press reported the raid thus:

Tasmanian Advocate, Dec 1, 1939

The attack took the German defences completely by surprise, said an RAF spokesman today. Enemy fighters did not engage the attackers, and no German planes were observed during the return flight. The objective was reached 20 minutes before darkness set in the leading section swooped down on three seaplanes seen on the slipways. Machine guns on the roofs of the hangars and pompoms opened fire when the defenders recovered from their surprise. Ships also opened fire. The RAF officers turned their machine guns on the seaplanes and defences, and then withdrew safely. All Returned Safely.

German communique admits that British planes, 'attempted to raid the air base at Borkum Island'. It claims that no damage was done, and that the RAF machines were unable to reach objectives on the German coast. In response to German statements to the contrary, the Air Ministry declares: 'All our machines returned safely from the RAF night reconnaissance over north-west, Germany last Monday. There is no truth whatever in the German allegation that our aircraft crossed Holland'.

Courier-Mail Special Service and Australian Associated Press

SEAPLANE BASE

British Fighter Bombers Score

LONDON, November 29. A British long-range fighter patrol made a dramatic raid on the German seaplane base at Borkum, in the Friesian Islands, yesterday. The raid was carried out in daylight and was the most audacious made since the RAF attack on the German naval bases at the entrance to the Kiel Canal on September 4. The Daily Mail reveals that for the first time new long-range fighter-bombers were used. Although it has not yet been reported officially, it says, 'it is known that the British machines did considerable damage,' adds the Daily Mail. 'British bombers would have difficulty in avoiding 'archie' fire. Therefore, it is very significant that we possess fighters capable of such 600 mile flights. They are destined to play a big part in the future.' The squadron was seeking the German minelaying seaplanes when it dis-covered Borkum, which the squadron presumed was the mine-laying base. Although the squadron carried no bombs, the pilots decided that the opportunity was too good to miss. The machines hurtled down in power dives on the seaplanes, which were sprayed with machine gun bullets from an altitude of a few hundred feet.

'The attack took the German defences completely by surprise', said an RAF spokesman today. Enemy fighters did not engage the attackers, and no German planes were observed during the return flight. The objective was reached 20 minutes before darkness set in the leading section swooped down on three seaplanes seen on the slipways. Machine guns on the roofs of the hangars and pompoms opened fire when the defenders recovered from their surprise. Ships also opened fire. The RAF officers turned their machine guns on the seaplanes and defences, and then withdrew safely. All returned safely.

German communique admits that British planes, 'attempted to raid the air base at Borkum Island'. It claims that no damage was done, and that the RAF machines were unable to reach objectives on the German coast. In response to German statements to the contrary, the Air Ministry declares: 'All our machines returned safely from the RAF night reconnaissance over north-west, Germany last Monday. There is no truth whatever in the German allegation that our aircraft crossed Holland.

Biggin Hill had once again been front and centre but more was to come and nobody could have predicted the level of destruction which would be meted out to this Kentish airfield.

Note (1) 'Willie' Rhodes-Moorhouse DFC - No. 601 Squadron was re-equipped with Hawker Hurricanes, moved to Tangmere in March, 1940, and took part in the Battle of France, mainly flying from Merville (the same airfield from which his father had flown in WW1). Returning to the UK, No. 601 Sqn was heavily engaged in the Battle of Britain, suffering many losses, including William who was shot down on 6 September, his Hurricane crashing near the High Brooms railway viaduct near Tunbridge Wells. He is buried beside his father on a hill within the grounds of what was the family home at Parnham House, Dorset.

Note (2) The small garage purchased by Rhodes-Moorhouse is now a car sales site. Post war, it continued to have a chequered career when the small detached house that formed part of the station was bought by the notorious East-End villains, the Kray brothers in the 1960s, as a safe house south of the Thames. Several of their henchmen were apparently billeted there when being hunted by the Police or rival gangs.

Note(3) Sqn/Ldr MF Peacock, No. 85 Squadron, was killed on 20 May the following year whilst flying Hurricanes from Merville. He was probably shot down by Haupt-mann von Selle of Stab II.JG3.

CHAPTER ELEVEN

THE WAR COMES TO BIGGIN HILL

18 AUGUST 1940

On a sunny Sunday, 18 August 1940, Marjorie Hallworth, aged 10, had gone to play with her friend, Charlie Williams, who lived further down Leaves Green Road towards Bromley. Marjorie lived in Leaves Green Crescent, a group of eight semi-detached houses on the western edge of Leaves Green Common, opposite the 17th century pub, the King's Arms. Her father was the local policemen but on this Sunday he was a little way from home, helping to bring in part of the harvest. At lunchtime Charlie's mum told Marjorie she ought to go home for her lunch in case it spoilt, but that she could come back down afterwards. She never saw her again.

On the left:
'Chippy' Manchip.

'Chippy' Manchip was a young man who had been brought up in Bromley, Kent. From the outbreak of war he had been busting to get into the services and do a bit. However, he found himself in what had been designated a reserved occupation and numerous attempts to release him from its constraints had failed. Not to be completely out of it, Chippy volunteered for the LDV (Local Defence Volunteers) as soon as they were formed in May 1940. On Sunday 18 August he had duly reported for the parade at Keston Mark (the parade ground was in the area now covered by Ravenswood School) and, after inspection, his company had been instructed to take up positions on Layhams Farm, about a mile west of Biggin Hill Airfield. Between their positions and the airfield was a valley known as Furze Bottom, with the ground rising towards Biggin Hill and covered by Miller's Fruit Farm (now Keston Fruit Farm). Chippy worked close to Croydon Airport and had seen the damage wrought by the *Luftwaffe* three days before when Messerschmitt Me.110s of *Erprobungsgruppe 210* had attacked on the evening of the 15th. He was therefore keyed up to see some action but could never have imagined what he would see on that Sunday morning.

Members of 'C' Company Home Guard on Lewis Gun practice.
Manchip is firing the weapon. (Edward Williams)

At Cormeilles-en-Vexin, in occupied France, the crews of *9/KG76* were preparing for a mission. Their aircraft were Dornier 17Z-2s and the unit was part of the 9th *Staffel* (Squadron) of *Kampfgeschwader* (Bomber Wing) No. 76. They were low flying experts and had gained a huge amount of experience during the invasion of Poland, during attacks on the Low Countries and in the Battle of France. On 18 August they were to take part in one of two highly choreographed raids on Kenley and Biggin Hill airfields. The plan was that aircraft from KG76 would wave-hop across the channel, make landfall on the Sussex coast near Beachy Head, and then continue at tree top level until they had to heave back on the stick to mount the North Downs and appear over the perimeter of Kenley airfield. Two days earlier a similar mission had been mounted but due to bad weather and some mechanical problems the raid had been aborted. Pilot, *Oberleutnant* (Flight Lieutenant) Rudolf Lamberty, chatted with *Hauptmann* (Captain) Roth who was to go along as one of the crew. At another E-Pen close by *Flieger* (airman) Rolf von Pebel checked his Leica camera and spare rolls of film; his job was to photograph the raid. As lunchtime approached, the flare to call the crews to readiness was fired high into the sky over the base and each aircraft became a hive of activity as the crew donned their kit and mounted up, whilst ground crews prepared to start the bombers.

Some years ago a document emerged which recorded the events of 18 August from the German perspective. It is called a *Gesfechtsbericht* (Operation Report) and, to show another aspect of that fateful day, is introduced in sections throughout this chapter. It shows an interesting balance of optimism and anxiety and finally the realities of a combat mission.

It begins with a section by Flieger (Airman) Bankhardt and appears to be a record of an aborted mission, probably on 16 August – their targets were Biggin Hill and Kenley.

Clear, sunny cloudless skies were the first things we noticed in the morning, as we always first looked at the weather. Would this day bring the big operation we hoped for against England? Two days we have already spent on high alert at our E-Pen. Flying suits and lifejackets were a bit uncomfortable in the oppressive August heat. The car again took us to the field out of town. The machines were not standing covered as usual in their camouflaged dispersals, but had been rolled out and were ready for use. We all felt here was something in the air, but it was the squadron commander who would deliver the decision. We heard him honk his horn from a distance, as he drove his car to our pit and that always meant something. He did indeed bring the orders. With a brief few words the targets were given and the start time ordered for 09:49. 'You are with *Leutnant* F. and hopefully bring us a few good photos, with the fighter escort it should be a Sunday afternoon outing, a harmless pleasure', the squadron commander said to me. So towards the obedient 'Gustav' the steel-gray bird that should carry the crew as well as me to England. Flying helmet on, Leica [camera] stowed and the machine was ready to roll to the start.

The metal birds soon floated in the air, others came to join us and formed into a squadron flight, as had been so often practiced. My thoughts at this moment went towards my comrade, at the front of the chain, who is joining the attack as a reporter. Will this flight bring us the great experience of which we have so often talked on quiet evenings? My thoughts were suddenly interrupted by the call of the radio operator: 'Sir, I have just received the radio message, to divide our Wing into Squadrons and return to home base.' 'Bloody hell,' muttered the pilot and turned as ordered. Shortly afterwards he set the plane down smoothly in spite of the heavy bomb load.

Stanley Dudley Pierce Connors had been born in Calcutta and educated in Darjeeling. His family returned to England and he joined No. 500 Squadron Auxiliary Air Force in 1936. He applied for a short service commission in 1937 and began training with 5 Flight Training School, RAF Sealand, in December, winning his wings and joining No. 111 Squadron at Northolt in June 1938 as a Pilot Officer. In May 1940 the Squadron began to fly patrols over France and Connors soon began to build an impressive score. On 18 May he destroyed a Junkers Ju 88 and a Messerschmitt Bf 109 and the next day he claimed no less than three Heinkel 111s and another Ju 88. On 2 June he was credited with damaging two Messerschmitt 110s over Dunkirk and five days later he claimed another Me.109. Technically he had become an 'Ace' (five kills) and

Stanley Connors
(Via Colin Brown)

No. 111 Squadron at Wick. Stanley Connors is standing, second from the right with sun glasses. (Via Colin Brown)

was awarded the Distinguished Flying Cross (DFC).

With his burgeoning experience he was appointed as a flight commander and continued to add to his score of victories. By 18 August he had claimed another four enemy aircraft destroyed and two damaged; he was a skilful and determined fighter pilot. At Croydon Airport he surveyed the damage that was being repaired following the raid three days before, awaiting the chance to even the score with his enemy. It wouldn't be long; as thoughts turned to lunch, the phone at dispersal rang.

The Dorniers left the French coast and dropped low over the sea, the object of the ultra-low flying was to avoid detection by British RADAR and to preserve the element of surprise. Certainly they were flying low enough not to become a blip on a cathode ray tube but could not avoid the most secret and technical piece of equipment available to the Allies, the auto-focus, self-cleaning Mk 1 human eyeball. The Observer Corps began filing reports to their HQ at Horsham as the nine German bombers crossed the coast and held their northward course. They were flying so low that photographer, Rolf von Pebal, took several fascinating photographs; one of which shows astonished pedestrians gawping as the German bombers hurtled past.

Remarkable images of the *KG76* Dorniers over the Channel and approaching the British coast. In the image below the Dornier is probably around fifteen - twenty feet from the surface of the Channel.(Chris Goss)

Dorniers of *9/KG76* approaching Beachy Head, again the altitude is remarkable, the shadows of the aircraft are almost directly below them, confirming the time of the attack. (Chris Goss)

The original plan had been that twelve Junkers Ju 88s would make a dive-bombing attack on Kenley, which would be followed, minutes later, by a high level saturation bombing by Dornier 17s. Minutes after this the nine low-flying bombers of 9/KG76 would arrive to attack targets of opportunity at Kenley which had survived the high level raid. However, things turned out differently as the first attack by the Ju 88s and the high level raids were delayed by the weather and fighter interceptions. This resulted in the low-flying Dorniers actually arriving before the air raid warning had even been sounded at Kenley.

Returning to the German report, the account by *Flieger* Bankhardt continues with a brief report on their successful high level raid on Biggin Hill from which they returned unscathed. They had bombed Biggin Hill as the Dorniers of *KG 76* were racing towards Kenley.

Bombs on aerodromes on the approach to London.

When the machines set to land after exactly three hours, I saw all the ground personnel on the runway. The men worried about us, and wanted to know if all their birds have returned undamaged. We climbed out of the machine, went to the comrades and shook hands with them. 'Boys, that was nothing, we had expected the defense to be a bit different'. Was that all the British can offer? Or has the Royal Air Force already been so weakened? *Flieger* Bankhardt.

Bombs bursting across Biggin Hill aerodrome, mainly at the eastern end of Runway 29. Smoke is rising from damage in East Camp. (Bankhardt)

Also on the high level raid was *Gefreiter* (Corporal) Willi Wanderer. His account follows on the next page and again seems to confirm that the RAF were caught unawares and the formation returned to base unscathed.

The bombing of a Biggin Hill airfield on 18 August 40.

After a futile flight on the 16th - we had to turn back at the channel because of problems with the plane - at last my wish was granted to take part in a major offensive. 'Get up', the first word of the duty NCO, woke me from my beautiful dream. First, look at the weather. A clear sky, so today it should happen. Put on the gear. A few sips of hot coffee and quickly to the lorry which would take us to the planes. Once there I felt very disappointed. The squadron commander told us that our destination would be Biggin Hill airfield, but at the same time, that our start would be delayed because of bad weather. So all we could do was wait. Lunchtime was approaching and suddenly we were told to start. The necessary equipment life jacket, parachute, oxygen had already been laid out. To put all this on and into the machine only took a few minutes and we were rolling to the start. There was fearful crowding. Flight control gave us the signal to start and in no time the whole squadron was roaring across the airfield. I just saw the ground staff waving and then the bird with its heavy greetings for England was in the air. Circling the airfield once we set course for England.

On our flight path to the coast other squadrons joined us. A wonderful sight the whole squadron - about 50 machines just like a practice flight. That things were becoming serious I could see from the command of the flight captain: Set up machine gun. I checked the two MGs twice to make quite sure, I would only have a few seconds to send a devastating burst of fire towards the English fighter planes. At the French Coast the promised fighter cover was coming nearer. To our left and right I now saw the whole sky full of black dots. It didn't take long -the channel was already shining deep blue below - when the dots started to whirl around. English fighter planes had started to attack. The altimeter showed us that it was necessary to switch on the breathing masks. In the meantime a white strip of coast became visible below us: the English Coast. Now we were expecting anti-aircraft fire but not a single shot was fired and unmolested we approached our targets. 'The bombs are falling', we were told. A look at the other machines, heavy parcels were raining down. Well, nothing will remain intact. With a hissing sound our bombs had dropped as well. Now a turn to the left and the target could be seen. A huge black cloud of smoke told us that the bombs had hit the target. A single anti-aircraft gun sounded but where were we? Not a single English fighter plane, no anti-aircraft fire came near us. Where are the English? We thought. But nothing moved, so without problems we set course for home. Not even my machine gun had a chance to become active. Pity - I would have liked to burn an English pelt. In sight of the French Coast we could fly lower and the breathing mask was no longer necessary. Time went quickly until we landed. We were bombarded with countless questions. For us there was only one answer: like a squadron exercise flight above the sleeping English. No one in the squadron had ever experienced such quiet hours during an attack. Is this already the end of the Tommys? Gefreiter (Corporal) Willi Wanderer

Rolf v. Pebal was flying with *KG76* and although he signs himself as a *'Flieger'* (Airman) in the report he was a *Luftwaffen Kriegsberichter*, a war reporter. Nonetheless, from the text it is clear he was full trained as an airman and was expected to man a weapon during an attack.

Report of the first low level flight over England with the 9th Squadron of *III KG 76.*

On the morning of 18 August we drove early to the resting place of our planes. On standby for a low level flight over England. One by one all our friends and comrades were arriving. There is great excitement. The start is again delayed for an hour then we are off. Strangely enough every one of us has an uncertain feeling, everybody has a foreboding that things won't go smoothly. The small pilot officer, Leutnant Wittmann, is the only one who voices his feelings, 'When the English join us today, the shit will hit the fan'.

At 13:20 hours we start, all nine planes of the ninth squadron. The tactic is to be: first of all the JU 88s of the second group are to dive bomb, then the Do's of the of the 8th squadron release their bombs, we should be able to destroy the targets completely in a low level flight. The operation should take place with strong fighter cover.

We are flying above the coast, over the channel, and are staying very low and are looking out for fighter planes. Haze is hanging over the water, drops are on the windows of the cockpit. Soon peace will be over. We see the coast shimmering through the fog, rise a few metres higher above the shallow haze and now we can see the English Coast very near and very clearly. I take as many photos as I can. About 600 metres we ignore two picket boats. They flash at us and when we don't answer they probably announce us to the anti-aircraft positions by radio as unwanted guests. But by then we are already above the cliffs. Now things get going. Doing about 300 kilometres per hour at 5 metres high, we are racing across English countryside. We use every ditch as cover, every wood to hide, we jump over trees, it's up and down all the time. I don't see any anti-aircraft positions. A fast train is coming towards us below and it's passed in a second. A couple on bikes are taking cover in the ditch, just as during our basic training. We speed across parks, big houses and palaces, across factories and drab workers' cottages. People who see the black crosses on our wings feel panic.

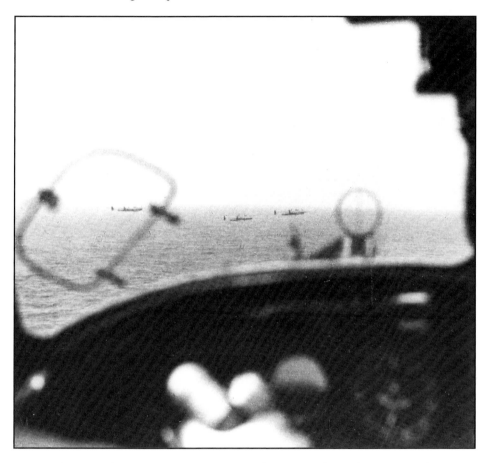

Another remarkable image, taken over the pilot's shoulder as the Squadron heads for the low haze mid-Channel. (Rolf v. Pebal via Chris Goss)

Beginning a right-hand turn, the formation is remarkably close as they
sweep towards Beachy Head. (Chris Goss)

Low flying in the extreme. A section of railway line which is captioned
as being in South-East England. Below: captioned as being East
Grinstead. Something of a surprise for those walking in the road.
(Above Hinze below Hinze via Chris Goss)

Low over open country, another Dornier visible on the skyline. Below: Rooftop flying over another suburb. (Rolf v.Pebal via Chris Goss)

The situation had become clearer to the fighter controllers as the Observer Corps reports continued to log the progress of 9/KG76. At Croydon Airport, the pilots of No. 111 Squadron leapt from their chairs as the scramble bell clanged and they were vectored to intercept the Dorniers. The pilots were astonished to be told to head towards Kenley and to 'Make Angels' (climb to altitude) one-zero-zero - one hundred feet'. Squadron Leader Thompson is reported to have replied to the instruction, 'Are you bloody mad? I could prune trees at that height!' The comment would have been clearly heard on the radio by one of his flight commanders, Flight Lieutenant 'Connie' Connors. Rushing towards Kenley just a few feet above the roofs of Purley and Caterham, Sqn Ldr John Thompson spotted the low flying Dorniers South of Kenley and had to make a snap decision. Would he lead his squadron against the nine enemy bombers head on or make a wide turn to bring his fighters into a position to make the classic attack from astern? In a split second he made his decision and ordered the squadron to follow him in a turn to attack the Dorniers as they reached the airfield perimeter.

At Kenley the airfield defences were quick to react and the PAC (parachute and cable) rocket defences were fired, each carrying five hundred feet (150 metres) of cable aloft to ensnare low level attackers. As the rocket reached the limit of the cable it would detach and deploy the small parachute which would keep the cable aloft for some time. The Dorniers pressed home their attack but, as was reported by Pilot Officer Ronnie Brown, who was in the vanguard of the 111 Sqn attack, the bombs were dropped too low to fuse properly and actually inflicted little damage. Brown came out of the turn astern of the Dorniers and opened fire on one of them, which crashed in Golf Road, Kenley, with all the crew being killed. He also 'squeezed off a few rounds' at another and claimed it damaged. This was almost certainly Rudolf Lamberty's aircraft as he later confirmed that he had been hit over Kenley, although he wasn't sure if it was by the Hurricanes which his own gunners were engaging or by ground fire. The only thing he was sure of was that his aircraft was still under control, his crew were uninjured and it was time to go home. He called for a course from his navigator and started a slow turn which would bring him onto a heading for the coast, a course that would bring him close to Biggin Hill.

Rolf v.Pebal's Dornier crossing the perimeter of Kenley airfield. A Spitfire can
be seen in the E-Pen over the top of the engine necel of the aircraft.
(Rolf v. Pebal)

Flieger Rolf v. Pebal continues his commentary:

Gradually we are losing contact with our group leader, the formation is breaking
up. Then an airfield. The last fighter plane has just left the ground and now the
English are trying to get at us in a wide sweep from astern, whilst our bombs turn
somersaults on their airfield and explode. A Spitfire latches onto a machine to our
right and can't be shaken off. We can see the tracer bullets wizz between the machines. Our radio operator is shooting. A fighter plane comes close on our tail. I've
stopped taking photos long ago - the fighter is getting bigger all the time and the
radio operator is putting up a heavy barrage. I see flashes and flares on the wings
of the English, those are his shots from MGs and cannon. There is an almighty roar
in our machine. My foot takes a dreadful blow, I'm convinced I've been hit, but I
can't find a hole in my boot, just carry on shooting.
Then it got him, a lucky bullet has finished off the fighter, he's suddenly crashing
against the trunks of a wood, shattered and already out of view. I see how the radio

operator gasps and pushes his steel helmet on to the back of his neck with oily and trembling hands whilst putting on a new drum of ammunition. Suddenly, a crash louder than the motor and the cockpit is wrecked. I'm immediately thinking of anti-aircraft hits. Looking back I just see a bent tree, stripped of leaves disappearing in a hollow. In the middle of England we have touched a tree top. Below us are houses, a London suburb. Twice we have to fight off fighter planes. We are heading home. We realise that there is something wrong with the machine. The observer at the front is often shooting at anti-aircraft positions, in a few seconds and we've passed. Now the radio operator shoots from the back at the fast disappearing target. At last we're at the coast. The fighter planes have gone, we can see nothing of our comrades. No sooner have we got water below us then the left motor begins to pack up slowly and then completely. The oil tank has been hit, there is no lubrication. We are sweating blood. Slowly the machine drags itself on with one motor pulling us sideways. We try to read each other's thoughts from our eyes. The steel pot sits on the back of our necks, our hair is tangled, sticks to the forehead, the veins are popping out, sweat runs in streams over our face and drips down from the chin.

They were still a long way from their base in France, what is only about 30 miles of sea seems to be an ocean when nursing a sick aircraft. In the meantime, at Leaves Green, Marjorie Hallworth had just arrived home when the air-raid sirens started and German bombers were heard and seen approaching. Instead of having her lunch she was bundled down into the newly-constructed air-raid shelter by her mother, Annie, and they were joined by their next door neighbours, Ethel and Rupert Lomas. This was a high level raid and soon the ground began to shake with explosion of bombs in and around the airfield. Many fell on what is now West Kent Golf course and some fell in Leaves Green. One fell at the northern end of Leaves Green Common, close to the ARP post No. 21 which was dug into the bank near The Crown public house. The bomb destroyed the southern end of Farringdon Cottages and caused severe damage to Summerhill, a detached Victorian house next door, but there were no serious casualties. Another dropped immediately to the rear of No. 2 Leaves Green Crescent, the Lomas's home, causing considerable damage to the house. Although the Lomas's had taken to the shelter next door at No. 3, it wasn't as safe as it could have been because a blast wall had not been constructed in front of the doorway and, as a result the force of the explosion, all four were killed in the shelter.

On Layhams Farm, 'Chippy' Manchip and his colleagues watched in awe

269

as the bombs fell and they heard the crump of explosions and saw columns of smoke rising from different locations. As they watched, their attention was taken by the roar of aero engines and the staccato bark of machine guns further up the valley towards Saltbox Hill. As they watched, a German bomber came into view, flying very low and streaming black smoke from one of its engines. Behind it flew a smaller aircraft, a fighter, and as the two grew closer it was clear that the fighter, too, was on fire. As the stricken bomber drew level with their position, overlooking Furze bottom, it turned due east and continued to descend. It was only now that they got a clear view of the Hawker Hurricane, which was burning fiercely, as it quickly lost height and crashed into the shoulder of the valley, leaving a burning heap of wreckage and yet another huge pall of black smoke rising skywards. Acting on instinct and running on pure adrenalin, Chippy and another member of the Company sprinted out of their position and ran towards the burning aircraft. He said they had some foolish notion that the pilot might have been thrown clear and needed help. Arriving at the scene they couldn't get too close to the wreckage because of the heat from the burning fuel, however, they could see that the pilot had indeed been thrown clear but it was also abundantly clear from the severe fire damage to his flying overalls, and to what they could see of him, that there was no chance he could still be alive.

In Leaves Green Road, Geoff Greensmith ran through his home, 'The Chequers', to see what was happening out at the front. There was a terrific roar as Rudolph Lamberty's Dornier narrowly cleared the roof and went on to crash land in the field at the back. In the front garden Geoff was confronted by the unconscious body of a badly injured German airman who was tangled up in the shroud lines of his parachute, which had barely deployed before he hit the ground (most probably *Oberfeldwebel* (Staff Sergeant) Geier who survived quite serious injuries to be sent to Canada as a POW (Prisoner of War) in 1941). Immediately prior to this, two other members of the crew had taken to their parachutes; *Hauptmann* (Captain) Peters was also badly injured in the low level evacuation of the aircraft but *Feldwebel* (Sergeant) Eberhard pulled his 'chute before he left the aircraft and was violently dragged out, injuring his hand, though his parachute deployed enough to set him down without further wounds. *Hauptmann* Roth and *Oberleutnant* Lamberty remained with the aircraft as it ploughed into Milking Lane Farm. Badly shaken and quite seriously burnt, Roth and Lamberty clambered out of the burning wreckage to be captured and taken to the sick bay at RAF Biggin Hill. They were later moved to Farnborough Hospital and then on to the Royal Herbert Military Hospital at Woolwich.

At the Fruit Farm, Chippy and his colleague had to stand guard on the burning wreckage of the Hurricane and the body of Stanley Connors. After a while some RAF personnel turned up from Biggin Hill, led by a sergeant. He examined Connors body and removed his 'dog tags', handing them to Chippy Manchip. That's how he was always able to remember the name of the pilot as he had to hold the dead man's ID disks until another crew arrived with a stretcher to take the body away to the mortuary; he said that he read the name over and over and it remained ingrained in his memory.

Connors' aircraft is sometimes found recorded as being shot down by friendly anti-aircraft fire and crashing near Wallington. However, in the process of seeking permission to explore the crash site on Miller's Farm, Keston, the Ministry of Defence confirmed their records agreed that this was the area from which Connors' Hurricane (R4187) was actually recovered by the RAF MU (Maintenance Unit). Given Manchip's eyewitness account and the official record there is no doubt it was Hurricane was flown by Connors; this opens a debate.

Two days earlier on 16 August, F/Lt James Nicolson was flying a Hurricane near Southampton when he was hit by fire from a Messerschmitt Me.110. Wounded in the foot and with damage to one eye, he also had a fatally wounded aircraft. The engine was running rough and the fuel tank on the Hurricane had been ruptured, feeding a rapidly growing inferno. About to bail out, Nicholson saw another German fighter and dropped back into his seat and brought the blazing aircraft around into a firing position. Firing the guns he inflicted terminal damage on the German aircraft which dived away to crash. Only then did Nicolson take to his parachute, then to be further wounded by a member of the Home Guard who fired at him with a shotgun. For his outstanding bravery he was to be presented with the only Victoria Cross awarded to Fighter Command in WW2. The similarities between Nicolson's actions and those of Stanley Connors are quite striking, so why wasn't Connors nominated for a VC or, for that matter, any decoration at all?

At first there may have initially been some confusion as to exactly whose aircraft was on Miller's Farm, although Connors body must have been positively identified. Confusion wasn't uncommon, for instance, in another case fairly local to Biggin Hill, there was to be confusion over the identities of three Hurricanes which had been shot down on 1 September. At the end of the day Pilot Officer Bryant-Fenn and Pilot Officer Noble, both of No. 79 Squadron, Biggin Hill, were in Sevenoaks Hospital, wounded, but of the pilot of the third aircraft there was no immediate trace, and Sergeant Hugh Mortimer Ellis of No. 85 Squadron, Croydon, was listed as missing. He had always joked with his colleagues that he would be lost in the sea because part of his name was Mortimer and similar to the French mort à Mer (loosely translated as: 'die at sea') and for years this was supposed to have been his fate.

However a Hurricane had been recorded as crashing in a field off Warren Road, Chelsfield, Kent, and at the time it had been recorded as L2062, Nobel's machine, which actually came down near Sevenoaks. In the event there was no rush to excavate the site; the RAF arrived from Uxbridge and removed the surface wreckage, including guns and ammunition, and left the deeply buried engine and other remains until later. Some two weeks later a recovery team arrived in Chelsfield to complete the job and were somewhat shocked to begin to recover human remains. Enough of the pilot's body was recovered for them to be buried, probably in plot number 128 at Star Lane Cemetery, St. Mary Cray, near Orpington. However, the identity was never established and that's where matters rested until 24 October 1992 when a group of aviation archaeologists identified the crash site and recovered some parts of an aircraft. Crucial among the pieces recovered was a heavy gauge piece of aluminium on which was clearly stamped 2673, apparent proof that it was Ellis's aircraft and not that of P/O Noble. They also found more skeletal human remains which were sufficient for an inquest to be held, and for the coroner, Paul Rose, to accept the remains were that of Sgt Ellis and for those to be buried in Brookwood Military Cemetery, near Guildford.

Stanley Connors in 1940, wearing the ribbon for his DFC. (Chris Goss)

Although a considerable diversion from our narrative this shows that the crashed aircraft could be misidentified (as was Connors') and that the actual site where Ellis died was also wrong (as are numerous references to where Connors' Hurricane came down). There are other questions implicit in the Ellis case, for instance, once they had recovered some remains, enough for a burial, why did they not go back and complete the job. It would have been self-evident that only a partial recovery had taken place and, further, why there appears to have been little or no effort to identify the remains, even though they were clearly associated with a crashed RAF aircraft. This serves to illustrate how it was a less than perfect science and one reason why Connors' story may have slipped by virtually unnoticed.

Then there was the political aspect. On 14 May 1940, the Secretary of State for War, Anthony Eden, had broadcast to the nation, announcing that a local defence force was to be formed of men between 17 & 65 who were not immediately eligible for military service. Those who wanted to come forward were to report to their local Police station to submit their details. The response was enthusiastic and in the first week 250,000 men had signed in, by July it had become a staggering 1.5 million. On 17 May, the LDV (Local Defence Volunteers) had become a legal entity as the Privy Council issued the Defence (Local Defence Volunteers) order in Council. Whilst this was in process Neville Chamberlain had resigned as Prime Minister, to be replaced by Winston Churchill.

As the LDV developed so did problems in the definition of its role, whether it was to be an armed annex to the regular constabulary or it was to take a more proactive military role. The concerns mainly arose from the lack of weapons and uniform and a lack of formal training. The counter-argument was that a large number of those who had volunteered had previously served in WWI and were both well trained and, in many cases, experienced in battle. Some had retained vestiges of their uniforms and many (a surprising number it emerged) had held onto or acquired service rifles and pistols, as well as shotguns which are lethal at close range. Churchill called for a report and on 22 June he laboured through the War Office document which didn't make for terribly encouraging reading. It was clear the role of the LDV had to be defined and springing from that would flow the necessary requirements in training and the provision of weapons and uniform. He also thought that the title was uninspiring, and proposed the Home Guard as an alternative, stamping his own brand upon the new command. Again there was resistance, not least because a million LDV armbands were in the process of being machined and printed. However, Churchill won out and on the 22 July the LDV was officially renamed the Home Guard.

An interesting history but what has this to do with Stanley Connors and the events of 18 August 1940? On Layhams Farm, Home Guard Private Chippy Manchip and his colleagues had witnessed the burning Hurricane pursuing the mortally wounded Do 17, piloted by Oberleutnant Lamberty as Connors continued to fire his guns until either the ammunition was exhausted or he lost consciousness. A few moments earlier another group of Home Guard, stationed about a mile and a half south-east of Manchip's position, had also seen the low flying Dornier and, under the instruction of their platoon commander, Bertie Miller, opened fire with their .303 rifles and were to claim they had shot the bomber down. Of course it's not impossible that it was indeed the case, but as someone with considerable experience of both firearms and aviation, I would suggest unlikely. From their position the German bomber would have been between half a mile and a mile away (.8 - 1.6 km). Technically within the range of a .303 rifle but to hit a moving target at between 800 and 1,700 yards (760 – 1600 m) is a big ask; to inflict terminal damage on a bomber, even bigger. Small arms fire is something to be respected by pilots as, for instance, many the American helicopter pilot was to learn in the Vietnam war, but at the range and under the circumstances which prevailed on 18 August, almost certainly not the cause of the 'kill'.

The Home Guard position from which it was claimed they shot down, or at least finished off, Rudolph Lamberty's Dornier. Note the full issue of weapons and uniform.
(Mike Brown)

So why was it so readily attributed to the Home Guard? As described above, there was some uncertainty surrounding Connors' fate and some documents and subsequent accounts in publications attribute his demise to friendly fire. But, again, for the reasons explained above, it is beyond doubt that Connors and his Hurricane came down just north-west of Biggin Hill airfield. Similarly Ronnie Brown, another pilot with No. 111 Squadron, reported that he saw 'Connie' over Kenley, 'Legging it off after one of the Dorniers'. In correspondence with Rudolph Lamberty in the eighties he was quite clear that he had been attacked by and chased by a British fighter and that his gunners had returned fire. He said that the numerous hits on his aircraft were like, '…handfuls of dried peas being thrown at the metal skin'. Bertie Miller of the Home Guard claimed to have shot at the belly of the bomber but Lamberty was quite clear that he was flying more than a kilometre west of Biggin Hill airfield to avoid anti-aircraft defences, and his intention had been to steer east once past the northern perimeter and try to head low level for the coast. Unfortunately his aircraft was severely damaged and on fire and he feared the main spar might burn through, allowing the wings to collapse. Thus he opted for the wheels up landing in the field at Leaves Green.

Whatever the complete truth of the matter there was an overwhelming imperative and that was to take the opportunity to attribute the 'kill' to the Home Guard, which had only been formed just four weeks before at Churchill's behest; it was an opportunity too good to miss to underscore the decision to take the military option. A posed photograph was taken showing the platoon in position but there are clues there to the propaganda aspect. With the Home Guard just a matter of weeks old, although taking on the mantle of the LDV and what few weapons and uniform had already been issued, the men in the picture have complete uniforms and all are issued with seems to be the P.14 rifle. Most experts on the Home Guard tend towards suggesting this was an extremely unlikely situation, and it wasn't until some months later, and in some cases a year or so on, that platoons could parade such uniformity. The platoon hardly lined up as a crack military unit either as Bob Ogley comments in his book, *'Biggin on the Bump'*, 'They included caddies from the nearby golf course, clerks, milkmen, two postmen and boys on holiday from Malvern College.' But it was politic to award the credit to the Home Guard at the time, but it also deprived Stanley Connors of recognition of what seems to have been an entirely selfless and hugely brave thing to do.

Stanley Connors' body was repatriated to his home town of North Berwick where he was buried. A few months later his daughter was born to his widow, Marjorie. In many respects he was an unsung hero and I believe it is entirely appropriate to revisit his story 75 years after the events took place, as well as mentioning the others who were affected that August day in 1940, and record them here. Chippy Manchip managed to escape from his reserve occupation and join the RAF later in the war. He trained in Canada to become a bomb aimer on Lancasters and completed several trips over Europe, including a raid on the Dortmund-Emms Canal and that on Dresden towards the end of the war; he died in Bromley a few years ago. Rudolph Lamberty spent the remainder of the war in a POW camp at Bowmanville in Canada and returned to his home town of Trier, in Germany, where he ran a cycle business until he too died in 2000. Charlie Williams and Geoff Greensmith still live in the Biggin Hill. None of them will forget that day in 1940 when the war first came to Leaves Green and to Biggin Hill.

The King's Arms Hotel at Leaves Green with cars burnt out on the forecourt following the attack on the airfield a few metres to the rear. (Blundel) Below: The poignent plaque on the Keston War Memorial which records the civilian deaths including the Hallworths and Lomas's.

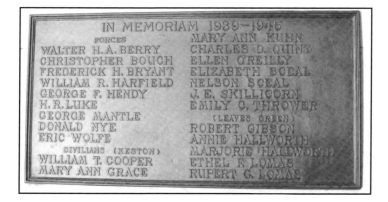

Left *Hauptmann* Roth, right *Oberleutnant* Lamberty. Both survived the crash landing at Leaves Green to be taken first to the Sick Bay at Biggin Hill and on to the Royal Herbert Military Hospital at Woolwich. Once fit to travel they were both sent to Canada as Prisoners of War. (Both Chris Goss)

Lamberty's Dornier at Leaves Green, the intensity of the fire is obvious from the damage. The swastika cut from the tail of the aircraft is in the RAF Museum, Hendon.(Both Edward Williams)

This rather poor image was snapped by schoolboy Terry Rothwell out of an upstairs window at his family home at Churchfields, just north-west of Biggin Hill Airfield. It shows the high level raid passing over and heading east for their bases in France. (T Rothwell via Edward Williams)

Right: Again snapped by Terry Rothwell from an upstairs window at Churchfields. In the distance, just to the right of the house opposite can be seen the smoke rising from Lamberty's Dornier at Leaves Green. Just below that can be seen a gathering of people in the street, no doubt shocked by immediate events. Just to the right of them is the local phone box heavily sand-bagged. (T Rothwell via Edward Williams)

Lamberty and his crew were not the only caualties from their Squadron, another Dornier had already crashed just outside the perimeter of RAF Kenley with the loss of the whole crew. Meanwhile Rolf Pebal watched as his pilot struggled to keep their damaged aircraft out of the Channel.

We are not yet in the middle of the channel. Not the time to take a dip in the drink, none of us have the desire or strength to paddle after this. We are at 10 meters but the cliff top is at 30 metres. To get up 20 m with one motor? We are trying to start the second motor, the pistons have seized up. The one motor pulls terribly, the pilot has to push his whole weight against it. We are prepared to get the dinghy ready, we all know that the chance of getting out of the machine before it's sinking is very slim indeed. We are all feverish. The plane rises a little bit, slowly drops again with a gust of wind. The coast is extremely near. We're crabbing along the cliff with the tail hanging down and gain a bit of height. There is a lower gap and the pilot risks it straight away. We manage it just, but it works. Now the plateau is dropping. At Abbeville the Corporal steering gets a cramp in his arm. We are looking for a place for an emergency landing. We believe we've found it. I put my steel-helmet on again - now a crash helmet - press my head against the ceiling and cling on with my arms, legs straightened out against something solid. The signal to lower the wheels sounds. We leave them retracted, only a belly landing can save us. The tension increases, I can hear the corn touch the plane. Or is it just the wind which whistles around the standing motors. A lurch, I close my eyes. Is that all? Now the feeling of drifting, a mad crash, banging jolting, creaking, grinding, and everything tumbles around. I'm pushed forward and down as if by a giant fist. At the same time there is thick smoke in the plane, a cloud of dust makes breathing impossible. For a moment all is deathly quiet, then everybody is pulling themselves together. Everybody pushes towards the exit. The emergency door won't open. If only the plane won't start to burn. Three of us push against the ceiling of the cabin which at last flies open with great noise. We are outside in a flash, our small radio engineer has both knees injured but the mad flight has reached its end.

Flieger Rolf von Pebal.

The *KG76* Dornier in which v.Pebal had been a crew member after a crash landing in France. The crew were largely unhurt and the aircraft was dismantled during the weeks that followed. (Chris Goss)

Above: A KG76 Dornier in a camouflaged dispersal undergoing servicing. Below War
Reporters Company 2 at Meudon near Paris, 1941, before deployment to Rumania.
Rolf von Pebal is sitting of the far right with hands folded. (Chris Goss)

C Company, 52nd Kent Battalion Home Guard in the gardens of 'Knightons', Westerham Road. On the ground in front (right) of them is a German MG 15 which was 'salvaged' from Lamberty's Dornier and pressed into service when weapons were short. Apparently it sat on top of a cupboard in Keston Junior School for many years after the war until somebody realised it was a live machine gun!(Edward Williams)

CHAPTER TWELVE

30 AUGUST 1940

THE WORST DAY

Following 18 August there was a brief dwell without too many raids or substantial damage to the airfield. However, on 30 August the airfields in 11 Group were again to receive devastation attention.

Station Operations Record Book:

30/8/40

12:00 - The Station suffered a high level bombing attack which did damage to the aerodrome surface and material damage to Biggin Hill village and Keston. The aerodrome surface was not rendered unfit for flying and aircraft still continued to operate.

18:00 - A low level bombing attack was carried out by the enemy on the Station and very serious damage was done to buildings and equipment. The raiders dropped 16 big H.E. bombs, estimated 1000 lbs weight each of which six fell among the buildings rendering completely useless and unsafe, Workshops, Transport Yard, Stores, Barrack Stores, Armoury Guardroom, Meteorological Office, and the Station Institute, and shattering by blast part of the airmen's Married Quarters which were being used as accommodation for W.A.A.F personnel. 'F' type Hanger in N. Camp was also badly damaged.
One shelter trench received a direct hit and two others near hits. The total ca-

sualties were 39 killed and 26 wounded and shocked.

All power, gas and water mains were severed and all telephone lines running NORTH of the camp were severed in three places.

Weather

Fair, cloud 4/10ths - 7/10ths at 1500' - 3000', wind 10 -15 mph N.Westerly, visibility 5 - 10 miles.

This was the worst single loss of life at Biggin Hill although attacks were to continue.

On 13 September, 1946, Gp Cpt. J Worrel, who had been Sector Operations Officer and second in command to Grice in 1940 as a Squadron Leader, wrote from HQ Transport Command to a Mr JC Nerney at the Air Ministry regarding the diary of a F/Lt RJB Jackson. Jackson had been Sector and Station Engineering Officer at the time of the attacks, though quite why the exchange was taking place in 1946 is unclear from the documents on file, but what it did achieve was to preserve for us copies of some extracts from Jackson's diary which are immediately relevant to our narrative. These are transcribed verbatim here:

Sunday August, 18th, 1940.

At approximately noon.

High level pattern bombing attack and aerodrome by 45 aircraft. One low level snooper shot down in flames on the edge of aerodrome. Approximately 500 bombs (500 kilo maximum) dropped on aerodrome. Direct hit on the M.T. sheds one bomb. No other damage to buildings. No damage to aircraft of vehicles.
Casualties:- 2 killed (One wireless Mechanic - One member of crew of Bofors gun) 3 airmen wounded. Approximately 90 D.A. bombs on aerodrome, positions marked. Enemy aircraft shot down by Biggin Hill sector. Aerodrome still operational.

The Friday, August, 30th

Noon.

A high level pattern bombing attack on aerodrome by aircraft. No damage to buildings or equipment etc. No casualties.

1800 hours.

Dive-bombing attack by JU 88's (1000 & 500 kilo bombs), nine aircraft. Severe damage to Technical and domestic area, to workshops, Equipment Section, Hangars, Airmen's Barrack Blocks, Dining Halls, Cookhouse, N.A.A.F.I. Sergeants Mess, Married Quarters, Guardroom, Shelters, main and camp roads etc. Electricity, Water and Gas Services, Main sewage and all telephone communications out. All M. T. dispersed - 90% damaged or destroyed. 2 aircraft (non-operational) damaged. 3 concrete air raid shelters hit.
Casualties killed - 1 officer, 40 N.C.O's and airmen, 1 W.A.A.F, 1 Soldier, 1 N.A.A.F.I girl, 1 civilian employee. Injured or wounded - 1 soldier, 1 W.A.A.F F/Sgt, 1 Officer, 1 civilian employee and several airmen and airwomen. Temporary service organized by Sector Signals Officer and Sector Engineering Officer. Fires under control. No further night work in Hangers repairing battle damaged aircraft possible. Rescue parties organised digging carried on all night to rescue victims in the Air Raid Shelters. Still operational. Several abortive attempt raids during the night.

A vivid description of the carnage which was wrought on the evening of the 30 August.

Amongst local doctors called to assist the injured and to certify the dead was Dr Mansi. Again I am indebted to Bob Ogley who wrote the following:

Ten years ago I wrote an obituary about an Orpington GP who was greatly loved and respected by his patients and friends. His name was Joe Mansi and he died in a nursing home at Bickley, aged 96.

I met Joe for the first time many years after his retirement when he told me he was the doctor who attended to the victims of the Luftwaffe bombs, which devastated RAF Biggin Hill after the horrific raid of August 30, 1940. An explosive had fallen directly into a trench shelter where 40 airmen and civilians were taking cover from low-flying Junkers. The bomb erupted with a detonation that echoed for miles around and left an enormous crater and scores of mangled bodies in its wake. In another trench, steel-helmeted W.A.A.Fs were packed together when an explosion blew out the entrance, the concrete walls caved in and the girls were buried under stone and earth. The entombed W.A.A.Fs were brought out one by one, the rescuers tearing frantically at the earth with their hands.

Dr Mansi was one of three doctors called to the scene of the first bomb. He found an opening but it was plain the majority of occupants had been killed. Those who were living and within reach were given a dose of morphia, several having injections in the face as this was the only part of them above earth. Six living men were taken out and Dr Mansi had to amputate the wrist of one to free him. When his gruesome night's work was finally at an end, Dr Mansi returned home to write his medical report on the most tragic night in Biggin Hill's history. Later it was reported he and Dr JC Colbeck of Downe and Dr Grant of Orpington had 'performed miracles' in the most macabre conditions imaginable.

A full list of the killed and injured is recorded in Appendix 4.

Returning to F/Lt Jackson's diary he continues to record the events of that tragic weekend, preserving a real flavour of the desperate fight at Biggin Hill.

Saturday August, 31st

Noon.

High level pattern bombing attack on aerodrome by aircraft. Further damage to buildings and services. No casualties.

18.00 hrs.

High level pattern bombing attach by aircraft followed immediately by dive bombing attack with J.U. 88's and 109's by aircraft, and ground strafing with Cannon fire by 109's. Further severe damage by direct hits on Hangars and other buildings. Dispersed MT and services etc. 4 aircraft and several vehicles received direct hits on ground with cannon fire and burned out. Direct hit on operations room, wounding Group Captain, R Grice, DFC Station and Sector Commander. Operations room completely destroyed by bomb and fire. Several more casualties among ground staff. During raid F/O Teddy Morris, severely wounded, crash landed his Hurricane in flames on aerodrome. Ambulance driver Sailor received immediate award MM for saving life of this Officer. 3 W.A.A.F's, Sgt H Turner telephone operator, Cpl EC Henderson, Clerk SO, both on duty in operations room at time and Sgt J Mortimer, armourer, received immediate awards of M.M. Fires under control by nightfall. Emergency Ops room brought into immediate use. Temporary services restored Unit personnel. Still operational.

Sunday September 1st , 1940

Morning

Salvage and dispersal of salvaged materials and equipment in progress.

Noon.

High level pattern bombing attack by aircraft on aerodrome. Further damage and casualties. Everything still under control and temporary services again restored.

18.00 hours.

Dive bombing and ground strafing attack. More damage and casualties. Still under control and services again restored. Fires soon under control. Still operational.

Monday, September 2nd. 1940.

Keston Riding School Stables taken over and salvaged workshop equipment installed. Tower Field house taken over and equipping as Main Ops room commenced. Rescue parties completed digging for victims in air raid shelters etc.

Thursday September, 3rd, 1940.

07.30 hours.

High level bombing attack. Practically nothing left to damage on aerodrome. Most damage to adjacent roads etc.

10.30 hours

Repeat performance. Still operational. Casualties :- 1 Sgt killed.

Wednesday 4th, September, 1940.

Quiet day.

Captioned as being Mary Cremin, the popular NAAFI girl, there may be others
in this image who were killed on the 30th August or subsequentlly.

Thursday September, 5th, 1940.

11.00 hours.

High level attack. Still operational. Installation of salvaged machinery in Keston Stables completed and normal workshop repairs commenced.

Bombing raids on Biggin Hill and the other front line stations were to continue throughout the early days of the war as the German Air Force pressed home *Unternehemen: Adler Angrief* (Operation: Attack of the Eagles) as a prelude to *Unternehmen: Seelöwe* (Operation: Sealion – the invasion of England). The strategy was proving successful with most of the front line RAF Stations in 11 Group in much the same shape as Biggin Hill. As F/Lt Jackson wrote above, 'Practically nothing left to damage on aerodrome'. At Biggin Hill what was left did nothing, according to Group Captain Grice, but attracted the Germans attention in an extremely unwanted fashion. He therefore asked the Royal Engineers to blow up the remains of the main hangars which, by that time, were beyond further use or practical repair, in the hope that the *Luftwaffe* would give Biggin Hill a little respite. Peter Brothers had been a Hurricane pilot with No. 32 Squadron and saw the damage and destruction at Biggin Hill first hand. When talking to him a few years ago he said that the Air Ministry had taken great exception to Grice's decision and had said they intended to charge him for damage to Air Force property. Pete Brother's response was characteristically short and to the point, he suggested Grice told the Air Ministry to take it out of his salary on a month by month basis. Apparently he heard no more of it.

Following what was thought to be the unplanned bombing of London, the RAF was sent to Berlin in a reprisal raid. This altered the German tactics and the Blitz began and was to last until mid-1941 Germany changed its focus and attacked the Soviet Union.

With the increase of night raids and with RADAR essentially blind behind the coast, the tracking of raids through this, the next phase of the war, fell to the Observer Corps for one part and, crucially, to the only effective means of detecting aircraft at night - the Sound Locators. Developed at Biggin Hill from the first crude concepts, the Mk IX Sound Locators did sterling service in guiding searchlights, and by extension, anti-aircraft guns on to their targets. The systems which brought the guns to bear and even aspects of the design of the guns and performance of their shells also had their roots firmly planted in the Air Defence Experimental Establishment, physical evidence of which has long since disappeared under industrial and housing development. However, in assembling the evidence in this work it is hoped the record of the crucial work undertaken at Biggin Hill for over twenty years before the Battle of Britain will be brought to the fore.

At the beginning of this book it was made clear that the concentration would be on these less well published aspects of the history of Biggin Hill, from Brooklands to the Battle of Britain; hopefully this has been achieved. Research has already begun on the next volume which will, again, focus in detail on aspects of the history of RAF Biggin Hill which, as with the first volume, are less publicised, but nonetheless an intrinsic part of our local and international history.

ACKNOWLEDGEMENTS

Thanks to individuals and organisations:

First and foremost my wife, Carol, for her proof reading skills and for helping sustain the effort required to research and develop this book.

Peter Bloomfield – for many good steers on local history.
Gordon Wright.
Paul Evans, Royal Artillery Library, Woolwich.
The Staff of the research facility, RAF Museum, Hendon
The Staff of the National Archive, Kew.
Judith Hay and the staff of Dartford Library - Kent Libraries, Registration and Archives.
Commonwealth War Graves Commission.
Laurie Chester - St George's Chapel of Remembrance
Terry Giles - for information on the Royal Observer Corps.
Lena Kroeger – the translation of German documents on the 18 August raid.
Rolf Steinhilper for his help with the above.
Tony Lewis - Biggin Hill Then & Now:
http://www.bigginhill-history.co.uk
Mike Brown – for his expertise on the Home Guard
Brenda Powell for information on Sir Oliver Lodge
Owen Leyshon of the Romney Marsh Countryside Partnership
Mrs Hilda Scarth
Mrs Stephanie McMurray
Edward Williams
David Wilcox

Special thanks to the late: Cedric Verdon

Reference works:

RAF Biggin Hill - Graham Wallace
Sir Oliver Lodge - WP Jolly
Romney Hythe and Dymchurch Railway - WJK Davies
Tizard - Ronald W. Clark
Communications: An International History of the Formative Years –
Russell W Burns
Echoes From The Sky - Richard N. Scarth
Most Secret War - RV Jones
Britain's Shield - David Zimmermann
Radar - How it all Began - Jim Brown
The Birth of British Radar - Arnold Wilkins OBE
Dowding of Fighter Command - Vincent Orange
Fifty Years of Brooklands - Charles Gardner
Radio Bygones - 1990 - Article by David Pritchard
The Shell Book of Firsts - Patrick Robertson
Bygone Kent V.7 No.12 1986 (P.740-743) - Michael Page
Bygone Kent - 1988 - Article by GW 'Gee' Smith
Open Cockpit - Air Vice-Marshal Arthur Gould Lee (P.164-173)
The British Mk IV Tank - David Fletcher (P.36)
Air Defence of Britain 1914-1918, Cole and Chessman.
'From Trenches to Cockpit' the diary of Air Mechanic James Marsden.
Air Enthusiast issue 102.
Kent History Forum
Institution of Electrical Engineers Journal Volume 59 - 1921 Report by
Major Erskine-Murray
The Theory of Anti-Aircraft Sound Location and Direction 1932 - WO.
History of RFC Wireless from the outbreak of War - Majors Orme &
Prince.
Finally the good company of Mark Fricker & Anthony Francis on several
fact-finding adventures, solid critique, and Tony's research on transport -
more of this in Volume 2 - *RAF BIGGIN HILL - From The Battle of
Britain to Biggin Hill Airport*

RAF BIGGIN HILL
FROM THE BATTLE OF BRITAIN
TO BIGGIN HILL AIRPORT

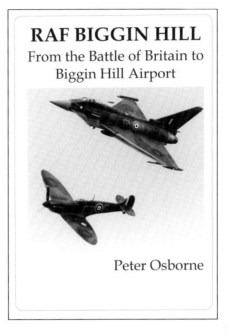

RAF BIGGIN HILL
From the Battle of Britain to
Biggin Hill Airport

Peter Osborne

This is the working title for the second and final part in the history of this unique seat of aviation and defence. As the direct defence of the realm became less of an issue, the fight was taken to the German forces occupying France. From this the airfield changed its role throughout the war, finally becoming a centre for the repatriation of casualties from the fighting in Europe and then the return to British soil for Prisoners of War.

In this second volume several other unique aspects of RAF Biggin Hill's history are unfolded in detail, the Operations Rooms, a Prisoner of War Camp within the perimeter, the full story of the Memorial Chapel from 1943 – 2015, the Auxiliary Air Force Squadrons, a return to Fighter Command, the Trains that were named after Biggin Hill, and their fate, and the first complete record of the effort to establish a suitable Heritage Centre at Biggin Hill.

Once again, detailed research of archive documents and access to private collections will produce the second part of the history of RAF Biggin Hill.

Target release date: Autumn 2016. If you wish to be notified of the release of the second book please send your details by email to:

Independent Books: mail@indbooks.co.uk

APPENDICES

APPENDIX 1

JOYCE GREEN

CASUALTIES RECORDED IN ST ALBANS CHURCH DARTFORD

Name	Rank	Date of RFC/RAF Accident	Buried
Barton HW	Flight Cadet	2/7/1918 RAF	Whitby
Brown CD	Flight Cadet	27/7/1918 RAF	Barking
Dow AG	2nd Lieutenant	7/8/1917 RFC	Dartford Watling St Grave A 635
Ferguson B	No record		
Fleming RJ	2nd Lieutenant	29/1/1918 RFC	Edinburgh
Griffith HH	Captain `	2/11/1917 RFC	Newtimber Churchyard, West Sussex
Gunther HH	2nd Lieutenant	18/7/1918 RAF	Dartford Watling St Grave A 1649
Henderson HG	Sergeant	29/9/1918 RAF	Newcastle-Upon-Tyne
Ideson JH	2nd Lieutenant	13/3/1917 RFC	Ilkley
James B	Captain	7/5/1918 RAF	Beeston Regis
Leduc JCR	Lieutenant	7/11/1917 RFC	Dartford Watling St Grave A 686
Litchfield FG	Lieutenant	24/9/1917 RFC	Darenth St Margaret's

Lonnen LEJ   2nd Lieutenant   16/8/1916 RFC   West Norwood
(Initials reversed on Cemetery Memorial)

March WH   Sergeant   24/4/1918 RFC   Dartford Watling Street
                                                                 Grave A 1651

Mapplebeck GWR Captain (DSO) 24/8/1915 RFC   Stretham Cemetery
                                                                 Grave P 528

Nash G   2nd Lieutenant   7/5/1918 RFC   Footscray Baptist
                                                                 Chapel yard

O'Connell CW   Lieutenant   18/6/1918 RAF   Leytonstone
                                                                 St Patricks

O'Hanlon SE   Lieutenant   3/2/1918 RFC   Manchester
                                                                 Crematorium

Owen N   2nd Lieutenant   3/6/1918 RAF   Llandudno
                                                                 St Tudno

Salmon WG   2nd Lieutenant   7/7/1917 RFC   Dartford Watling St
                                                                 Grave 1655

Simpson D   Cadet   20/11/1918 RAF   Inverness

Shield FL   2nd Lieutenant   2/6/1918 RAF   Birmingham

Taylor VS   2nd Lieutenant   14/1/1917 RFC   Wandsworth

Thompson CRJ   Captain   17/7/1918 RAF   Dartford Watling St
                                                                 Grave 1649

Van Rynevell JP Lieutenant   2/6/1918 RAF   Dartford Watling St
                                                                 Grave 1650

Wadlow H   Captain   1/5/1917 RFC   Frenchay, Stapleton,
                                                                 Bristol

Ward JG   2nd Lieutenant   7/5/1918 RAF   Bolton

Wheelock CH	Lieutenant	19/3/1918 RFC	Dartford Watling St Grave 1653
Williams CH	Lieutenant	2/8/1918 RAF	Dartford Watling St Grave 1648

Source: Commonwealth War Graves Commission

APPENDIX 2

Operations of No. 141 Sqn

Note: references to 'Giant' and 'Giants' which will follow are a generic term often associated with the German heavier than air raiders of WW 1. The principal long range bomber of the *Luftstreikräfte* (Imperial Air Force) was the Gotha G.V but the Zeppelin-Staaken *Riesenflugzeuge* (Giant aircraft) was also encountered on the Western Front and crossed the Channel to bomb England. This was shortened to 'Giant' or Gigant' and used to describe the German raiders. Much as in the same way the lighter than air machines were all called Zeppelins although many were built (including the first one to be shot down) by Schutte-Lantz

Combat patrols 1918, night.

16-17 February. 4 Giants raid London and Dover.

141 Squadron flew 4 sorties out of a total of 60 RFC/RNAS sorties. (4/60)
Aircraft: BE12
C3195 Lieut J.S. Castle.
A6308 Lieut E.J. Stockman, returned engine trouble.
C3210 Lieut E.E. Turner, wireless telegraphy tracker aircraft.
A6305 Lieut E.J. Stockman, later flight.
No contact.

17-18 February, 1 Giant raids London. (5/69)
Aircraft: BE12
6534 Capt E. Powell.
C3210 Lieut A.F. Barker.
6181 Lieut A.M. Bennett.
6138 Lieut E.E. Turner.
BE12B C3152 Capt N.H. Dimmock.
No contact.

7-8 March, 5 Giants raid London. (3/42)
Aircraft: BE12
C3195 Lieut J.S. Castle.
A6308 2nd Lieut J. Hetherington.
C3210 Lieut W. Hunt.
No contact.

No. 141 Squadron April 1918.

A Flight
Re-equipped with Sopwith Dolphins. By late April, 3 Dolphins and 5 Bristol Fighters had been received:

Bristol Fighters: C844, C858, C868, C875, C880.

B Flight
Bristol F2B Fighters.

C Flight
BE12.

It had been planned to equip the squadron entirely with the Sopwith Dolphin, but these were found to be unsuitable for night flying and suffered from poor engine reliabity.

19-20 May, 28 Gothas raid London (7/88)
Aircraft: Bristol Fighter
C820 Lieut E.F. Haselden, Lieut R.C. Cowl.
C823 Lieut Kelsey.
C4715 Lieut F.R.S. Southon.
C851 Lieut E.E. Turner, Lieut H. B Barwise (Biggin Hill's first 'kill')
C4778 Capt B.E. Baker.
C863 2nd Lieut A.K. Bamber, 2nd Lieut G.R. Barker.
C875 Lieut H. Slingsby.

APPENDIX 3

RAF Personnel killed in the shelter on 30th August 1940:

Cpl.	Alfred Baker
AC2	James Barnett
LAC	Thomas Charles Joseph Brunning
AC2	Archibald Charles George Burton
LAC	Edwin Henry Fredrick Butterfield
ACW1	Edna Lenora Buton
LAC	Deric Henry Mervyn Carter
Cpl	Percy Cecil Clark
AC1	Herbert Crane
LAC	Richard Cross
AC2	James John Juillen Dyning
AC2	Douglas Arthur Emery
AC1	John Albert George
AC2	Arthur Hudson
Cpl	Bertram Archibald George Imeson
AC2	Leon Moors
Cpl	Walter Herbert Ronald Mumford
AC2	Denis William Murton
AC2	Joseph Musgrove
AC1	John Joseph Jackson
LAC	George Edward Riggs
AC2	William Snaddon
AC2	Eric Harry Stopher
AC2	Edward Thomas Veal
Cpl	Richard Wemyss White
AC2	John Leonard Whitford
AC1	Albert Lane Wren
AC1	William Wright
F/O	Peter Desmond Leigh Yorke

Added to this terrible toll was Sapper John Ketteridge from 703 General Construction Company Royal Engineers and Mary Cremin from Cork in Ireland who worked for the NAAFI.

Injured

AC2	Robert Cecil James Baker
Cpl	Walter Chesters

AC2	Herbert Howard Clark
AC2	William Curruthers Bauchop Duncan
Cpl	Ellis Heaton Fealey
AC2	Reginald Frank Flowerday
AC2	Frederick Harris
AC2	William Richard Lewis
LAC	John Moore
AC2	Septimus Simpson
AC2	Frederick William Townsend
AC2	Harrold Whalley
F/O	John Mitchel Welshman

Civilian casualties in Biggin Hill Village and surrounding area:

Norman Arthur Roberts
Herbert Benjamin Lowe
Frank Shae Longman
Thomas Evans
Thomas Curtis

Leaves Green

Majorie Hallsworth
Annie Hallsworth
Ethel Lomas
Rupert Lomas

APPENDIX 4

OBITUARY NOTICE

Dr (Major) William Sansome Tucker

William Sansome Tucker, who died on 3rd July 1955, in a nursing home in Canada, will be remembered by many as the originator of the hot-wire or ' Tucker' microphone which gave splendid service to the British Army sound-ranging sections in the 1914-18 war. Tucker, already approaching middle age, first joined the Army as a private and was later posted to the Experimental Sound-Ranging Section at Kemmel Hill in Belgium (commanded by WL Bragg (now Sir Lawrence) where he quickly rose to commissioned rank. In 1916 the new art of locating enemy guns by sound - that is, sound-ranging - was in serious difficulty because the microphones then used to record gun sounds lacked the ability to give a clear ' break ' indicating the time of arrival of the sound because they were in a nearly continuous state of agitation from the noise of firing. Tucker had the inspiration to use a heated platinum wire mounted in a small hole in the wall of a container, such as an oil-drum, and to record the sound from a small change in the electrical resistance of the wire caused by the rnovement of air into and out of the container during the passage of a pressure-wave. This device was an immediate success and became the standard unit for sound-ranging sections in the British and American armies. The merit of the invention was recognized by the British and American Governments after the war by the granting of ex gratia awards. Tucker was also awarded an OBE.

After the end of the 1914-18 war, Tucker was engaged by the Royal Engineer Board of the War Office to carry out experiments and research into ways of detecting aircraft by sound at great distances and into ways of improving the accuracy and effectiveness of the sound-locators used to guide anti-aircraft searchlights. He collected round him a small group of scientists and technicians for the purpose and eventually became the Scientific Director of the Air Defence Experimental Establishment. He made valiant efforts to achieve the kind of results required for military purposes and made many great advances, but owing to the ever-increasing speed of aircraft the task became more and more difficult and by about 1936 it became clear that no acoustical rnethod of detecting or locating aircraft could meet future operational requirements satisfactorily. Fortunately, it was at about this time that the possibilities of RADAR began to he realized.

Tucker was born in Taunton of Somerset parents and was 79 years of age at the time of his death. As a young man he gained a National Scholarship which took him to the Royal College of Science at South Kensington where he earned a First Class Associateship (1901) and BSc. (Hons) (1903) under Sir Arthur Rücker as professor. He was noted for his experimental ability and his expert manipulation of delicate apparatus. While at South Kensington he carried out post-graduate research under HL Callendar which earned him a Doctorate of Science in London University. Prior to the 1914-18 war he had been for many years a lecturer on physics at West Ham Technical Institute. After his retirement from Government service (about 1940) he resumed teaching activities in Durham University and continued there to the end of the Second World War. Later, with his wife Grace (nee Morris) he went to live with his married daughter, Beryl Mutton, in Canada. His wife pre-deceased him by some two years.

Tucker was an ardent supporter of the Physical Society and at his death had been a fellow 50 years. He will be missed and mourned by his many Physical Society friends.   ET Paris

APPENDIX 5

PRESENT DAY

Here are presented several images of structures which have survived as monuments to Biggin Hill history. Most are easily accessible and well worth a visit.

DUNGENESS

The 200 ft mirror as in 2015.

In the foreground the 20 ft mirror and in the background the later 30 ft unit.

Above: The 20 ft mirror from the front. First to be erected at the Greatstone site. This was first level design which still required an operator to stand outside in the elements. Below: The 30 ft mirror which incorporated many advances in acoustics, the angling back, the larger diameter and the sound collector which was moved around from inside the control room, thus taking the operator inside for the first time.

The 30 ft mirror from the rear showing how it was constructed from a series of flat shuttering elements. The wedge-shaped structure bottom right, is the staircase to the control room which was once at ground level. See also next image and that on P 117.

Steps to the control room of the 30ft mirror.

The entrance to the control room of the 30ft mirror. The remains of the control mechanism for the sound collector hangs from the ceiling. An interesting comparison with the period image earlier in the book (P 118)

Above: Looking into the control room from what was once a glazed window. Again the remnants of the sound collecting mechanism can be seen protruding from the ceiling.
Below: A panoramic view of the 200 ft wall

Above: The 200 ft wall and forecourt. In the distance Dungeness Power Station.
Below: The end of the wall showing that the rear buttresses did in fact protrude in the
same way as the Maltese wall. It was just that the forecourt covered them, but has
dropped away at the end due to gravel extraction and collapse.

The rear of the wall showing the buttresses and the impressions in the concrete of the fine shuttering by the Royal Engineers.

The rear of the wall showing the remains of the control room and stores. It is
said to have collapsed, but my view is that it might have been the victim
of experiments with explosives. See also the next illustration.

Above: There are two or three similar penetrations of the buttresses at the rear of the wall. Experience leads me to believe these are the results of experiments with 'shaped' explosive charges. There is also evidence of the impact of small arms fire on the rear wall. Below: Remaining evidence of the bridge that was built to take the full size railway line to New Romney over the spur line from the RH&D miniture railway.

315

Above: The view through the bridge over the War Office spur line. The 200 ft mirror can be seen in the distance. Below: The mirror at Abbot's Cliff near Dover.

The 30 ft parabolic bowl at the Hythe site on 'The Roughs', sadly now in a poor
state of repair. The solid mirror which stood on the site fell forwards
during a land slip some years ago. (2014)

The concrete bunker on 'The Roughs' above Hythe, Kent. It is situated just below the position of the original sound mirror and the more advanced design, shown on the previous page. However the case has never been conclusively made for it being part of the ADEE Acoustic Research site. (2014)

INDEX

Rowe, AP	211,214,215,233
Royal Air Force	20,29,39,54,56,103,198,212,214,218,226,236,239, 243,245,250,251,256,260,261,271,272,273,276, 291,301,
Royal Arsenal, Woolwich	12,110,
Royal Artillery	91,
Royal Engineers	15,18,27,37,47,76,83,91,110,121,122,143,291,301,303,313
Royal Flying Corps	12,15,16,19,20,2425,26,27,28,30,33,35,36,39,44,47,51, 54,68,72,73,92,191,200,213
Royal Herbert Hospital Woolwich, Kent	271,278
Royal Navy	18,19,20,51,54,73,81,82,133,136,198,201,214,215,217, 218,219
Royal Observer Corps	52,73,156,189,198,216,217,224,226,234,242,243,257, 267,291
Royal West Kent Reg.	248
Saltbox	103,146,191,192
Saltbox Hill	229,270
Sassoon, (Sir) Philip	228,245
Scarth, Richard	197,201,202,203,294
School of Anti-Aircraft	See: Anti-Aircraft Defence School Defence (SAAD)
Signals Experimental Establishment (SEE)	47,89,92,104 (Report),110,129,132
Smith GW (Gee) LDV	37,294
Smutts,J, Lt Gen.	73
Sowrey, Lt RFC	52
Squadrons	
No. 6	25
No. 9	25,26
No. 10 (Training)	10,34,35
No.16	27,28
No. 22	232
No. 32	155,216,220,221,223,232,242,291
No. 48	155
No. 49	231,232
No. 56	72,105
No. 57	231
No. 62	52
No. 78	52
No. 79	223,248,272
No. 85	252,272

ADDENDUM

As with many things there are last minute changes, and this work is no exception. Contact had been made with Dr Tucker's granddaughter, Stephanie McMurray, who had some of her grandfather's original papers. The remainder had been in the charge of another of her relatives and had been donated to Trent University (Canada) where they remain and are beyond immediate reach. However, Stephanie was kind enough to forward the papers and images in her possession. It was clear there was enough material of immediate interest to include as an addendum to this work, and these follow.

They are mainly concerned with Dr Tucker's retirement from the ADEE, at about the time the establishment moved from Biggin Hill to Christchurch, Hants. Tucker, seemingly, didn't want to follow in his position as Director of Research. This was probably as much a consideration of the move itself, he was by then 63, as much as the radical change in direction of ADEE which had been precipitated by the advent of RADAR and its effects on defence. Dr Tucker's life's work had been in the field of acoustics and although Sound Locators were giving sterling service, and would continue to do so for much of the war that was to follow, cutting edge research now followed a different path.

The transcriptions of the letters which follow give both an impression of the affection which Dr Tucker felt for his staff and the pride for what had been achieved, and the reciprocal esteem in which his colleagues clearly held him.

Also transcribed is an article he wrote for 'Nature' (journal) in 1936, at about the peak of acoustic research and which spells out technically how sound locators work. It is a scientific paper but is quite accessible and gives an excellent insight into the logic and thinking of the time.

Lastly, an aerial photograph was sourced at the last minute which shows the War Office site at Biggin Hill, albeit in 1941. This has been reproduced opposite a copy of the site plan from page 93 for ease of comparison.

LETTERS

A.D.E.E.,
Biggin Hill.

9th February, 1940

Dear Colonel Evans

I am anxious to convey through you a special message to all my old friends in the A.D.E.E. I am proud to think that in this category I can include not only the officers but every individual with whom I have been in contact.

I have now had over twenty years' association with members of S.E.E. originally, and latterly A.D.E.E., and such association makes for friendships of long standing. I want to express, therefore, to them my gratitude for the happiest relations which have universally been existing, for the whole-hearted support they have given me and the enthusiasm with which that support has been given.

Although inevitable, the breaking of this association is being very keenly felt by me, and I cannot let the occasion pass without wishing them all a very happy future in their new activities and a continuation of that same spirit of co-operation and support for my successor and, for yourself.

May the A.D.E.E. flourish.

Yours very sincerely,

(Sgd.) W. S. TUCKER.

AIR DEFENCE EXPERIMENTAL ESTABLISHMENT
SOMERFORD,
CHRISTCHURCH,
HANTS.

19th February 1940.

Dr. WS Tucker,
33, Shortlands Road,
Bromley,
Kent.

Dear Tucker,

I have just learned from Evans that you are very kindly presenting your
I.E.E. Journals and other scientific publications to our A. D. E. E. library.
Evans and I appreciate your kind thought in so doing, and I feel sure that
the other members of the staff will also have cause to be grateful for this.

Yours sincerely,

(Signed)

DH Black

Black then penned a personal note which is reproduced overleaf:

'Kenwood'
Southcliff Road
Friars Cliff
Christchurch
Hants

22nd February, 1940

My Dear Tucker,

Many thanks for your letter which arrived this morning. I had intended writing to you in any case, as I did not consider my note of thanks for your library gift sufficient in iteself.

First of all, may I thank you for the way in which you handed things over to me. I very much appreciated the opportunity of overlapping you by five months, since it gave me the opportunity of being able to have your counsel and advice on men and matters. Moreover it gave me the opportunity of knowing you, which I should otherwise have missed. I hope our brief acquaintance will not be terminated by our official seperation.

I appreciate how hard it must have been to you to hand over your 'family' to the care of another, and a rank outsider at that. However, I hope you have not too many questions about their new 'father'.

I realise only too well that I have a big job in front of me; and although at times it might not seem so, I assure you I appraoch it in all humility. I hope to be able to make my contribution towards making ADEE one of the best establishments of its kind in the country. Evans is with me there and I feel we ought to have a very happy partnereship.

Rest assured that I shall not lose sight of Hodgkinson. I am anxious to have his group functioning from Christchurch as soon as possible. There are difficulties but we ought to be able to overcome them, and I want to have him nearer at hand in order to make greater use of his capabilities.

Once again many thanks for all your help during my initiation.

My kind regards to Mrs Tucker. My wife joins me in wishing you all the best. Yours sincerely, (Signed) DH Black

THE ARTICAL FOR 'NATURE'

It is a regrettable fact that some of our scientific activities have required the stimulus of war to initiate them and the fear of war to keep them alive. Not the least striking example of this impingement of military necessity on scientific research is afforded by the subject of direction finding by sound. During the Great War, sound provided the only means of locating the submarine that threatened our shipping, mining operations that threatened our entrenchments, the distant and invisible gun and the aeroplane flying behind cloud or in the darkness ; and this search by sound provided four widely differing methods all requiring advanced scientific technique. The subject is so large that I am proposing to confine myself to the Operation of finding the direction of sound transmitted through the air.

It is curious that, of air-borne sound, the War provided us with ideal sources - the gun and the aeroplane. The gun report is an almost perfect example of an impulsive sound - the anti-aircraft shell burst is even better. The aeroplane, so complex in the nature of its sound, has something so rich in its elements - high frequency, low frequency, impulsive, musical, non-musical - that it gives a fascinating mixture of qualities taxing the provision of many kinds of apparatus for investigating its properties.

The fear engendered by these characteristic sources - gun and aeroplane - has stimulated lines of scientific inquiry almost entirely dominated by military requirements, and such inquiries and the results of them have fallen into the category of secret investigations with all the handicaps of fettered scientific discussion. I will try, however, to strip my subject as much as possible of its war implications, and endeavour to show how fascinating the study of sound direction finding can become.

All living creatures equipped with listening faculties appear to have a capacity for obtaining the direction of sound, but this sense of direction is only provided by the functioning of two ears. When either a human being or an animal is deprived of hearing in one ear, sense of direction is very seriously impaired. What is called the binaural faculty has to be replaced by that of a single ear, in which reliance must be placed on variations of intensity due to the shadowing of the head. Even so small a creature as the cricket, using two ears, shows good directional perception, as has been shown by the direct flight of the female to the chirping male, and it has been shown that removal of the tympanum of one ear of the female deprives it of this capacity[1]. Some interesting experiments of Engelmann[2], working in the laboratories of Prof. D. Katz, illustrate the performance of a very intelligent sheepdog called 'Asti', one of whose ears was bandaged. The dog then lost its remarkable powers of direction finding. Some residual sound in the bandaged ear appeared to give partial help, but, in addition to exhibiting false judgments, the dog's reaction time changed from about 3/4 second to a mean of nearly 4 seconds.

What, then, is the function of the second ear? The answer appears to be perfectly easy when the sounds to be located are impulsive or of short duration. The ears owe their directive capacity to the fact that they are separated, and the distance between them is a determining factor. If the sound is directly in front, the sound arrives at the two ears simultaneously; if from the side, one ear receives the sound a very short time earlier than the other, the measure of that time being determined by the angle that direction makes with the median plane of the head, or with the line perpendicular to that joining the ears. From the known speed of travel of sound and the distance between the two ears, a time interval can be worked out for every direction, so that, if the brain recognises this time interval, a definite direction can be associated with it. A more accurate appreciation of direction can be given by turning the head until we face the sound, and this corresponds to the simultaneous arrival of the sound at the two ears. This time difference theory, enunciated by Hornbostel[3], has been supported by most modern exponents, and has been shown to be not inconsistent with the late Lord Rayleigh's theory of location by phase difference.

A very good example of direction finding by measuring time intervals is shown in sound ranging of guns[4]. Here the ears are replaced by microphones. Instead of the base length of only about 6 inches for the two human ears, the microphones were at the ends of a base from half-a-mile to three-quarters-of-a-mile long. The time intervals were therefore long and measurable by suitable timing apparatus, and from these any two microphones gave a direction, three gave two directions and an intersection, and therefore a location. Three more microphones were used in an Installation, in the War, making six in all, giving five directions and a mean of locations which improved the accuracy of location very considerably.

The unit of measurable time difference was then about 1/100 sec., and recent advances in sound ranging have made it possible to measure to less than 1/1000 sec.; but the human mechanism of time recording is very much finer than this. Thus, experiments have shown that the pair of human ears with the Interpretation of the brain can distinguish time intervals of 30/1,000,000 sec., and interpret them into a perceptible difference in direction. Animals can do even better than this. I am indebted to Prof. Katz for communicating to me some results obtained in his laboratories at the University of Rostock by Engelmann[2]. Engelmann's method of testing the faculties of animals exhibits great ingenuity. Two similar screens placed side by side served to hide a source of sound, and, on a hook behind the screen hiding the source, was placed a piece of sausage. A dog was trained to associate the correct choice of the screen with the reward of a piece of sausage. By adjustment of the screens both as regards distance from the dog and of their distance apart, the limitations of the dog in the correct identification of the screen gave a measure of the angular separation of the screens, and hence the capacity of the dog to separate directions of sound. The experiments were carried out with three dogs, the dog 'Asti' giving the remarkable performance of a separation 2° 9', corresponding to a time interval of 14/1,000,000 sec. A smaller dog, 'Fritz', gave even better results: a Separation of 1° 16' and time interval of 7/1,000,000 sec.

Experiments with cats, in which the source of sound was the rustle of two white mice in a cage, gave, in one case, a separation of only 48' and a time interval of 2.8/1,000,000 sec. Experiments with hens and chickens gave other figures showing how very sensitive to sound direction for certain sound these creatures are. Here the source of sound which served as a test for the hen was the 'cheep' of the chick, and the chicken was tested on the cluck of the mother hen.

The following table shows the relative capacities of the various creatures as regards accuracy of direction finding; man is obviously outclassed.

I have emphasized so far the time difference explanation of this phenomenon of directional listening; but it may be objected that the direction finding of a continuous sound like an aeroplane cannot be so accounted for, since we would appear to have no discrete pulses on which we can observe such time difference. I have already referred to the quality of aircraft sounds and have mentioned its partly impulsive character. However much help may be derived from what is called the phase difference between the waves of incoming sound, our experience with troops has taught us that it is these flutterings and pulses which appear to be given out irregularly that make direction finding easy. Even, when the source of sound is entirely musical, atmospheric irregularities make the sound appear to fluctuate, and it is the time interval between the arrivals of these discrete fluctuations or flutterings which give the binaural sensation so prominently.

Subject	Base-length between ears	Accuracy of direction finding	Distinguishable time intervals between the ears (10⁻⁶ sec.)
Man	14 cm.	4°18′	30
Dog :			
"Asti"	13 cm.	2° 9′	14
"Fritz"	9 cm.	1°26′	7
Cat	7 cm.	48′	2·8
Hen	3 cm.	2° 9′	3·3
Chicken	1·5 cm.	2° 9′	1·6

Now it must be admitted that this faculty of direction finding by sound grew naturally, both in men and animals, from the necessity of locating sounds nearly in the horizontal plane. With the advent of the aeroplane, we are faced with the necessity of listening to overhead sounds also, and here our listening mechanism shows a lack which it is probable Nature will never contrive to redress. When listening to the overhead sound, rotation of the head does not alter that time difference between the arrivals of the sound at the two ears upon which we depend for acquiring sense of direction, and this disability, although greatest in the overhead position, still persists, though in a gradually lessening degree, as the angle of elevation of the aeroplane is reduced. To get accuracies in the overhead position comparable with that of horizontal listening, the listener must make the axis of his body horizontal, that is, he must lie down with his length parallel to the course of the aeroplane before making use of his ears for direction finding. His head is then placed as well for locating the overhead sound as previously, when the body was erect, it was placed for locating sounds on the ground.

It may be that this uncertainty in placing an aeroplane which is overhead is responsible for the feeling experienced during the War that the bombing aeroplane seemed to spend an undue amount of time exactly over us, an impression, no doubt, which added to the terror of this overhead menace.

331

In the design of an efficient sound locator there is one obvious improvement to aid directional listening, namely, the artificial separation of the two ears. If we can, so to speak, pull the ears out of the head and separate them, we can increase for any given direction that time difference upon which a sense of direction depends. This pulling out of the ears can be done artificially by means of tubes placed in the ears with their open ends widely separated. If, further, the terminations of these tubes can be some type of sound collector, such as a horn, the improved directional properties can be supplemented by a magnification of the sound.

This was the fundamental principle which led to the design of the first British sound-locator, produced by the Anti-Aircraft Experimental Section of the Munitions Inventions Department under Prof. AV Hill. Four wooden horns were used on altazimuth mounting. The Operation of direction finding involves two pairs of ears and two pairs of trumpets. The azimuth listener uses the horizontal pair which rotates about a vertical axis, while the altitude pair rotates about a horizontal axis. In operation, all the trumpets in a frame move together so that their mouths always point in the same direction.

It must be noted also that the azimuth listener must be on the correct bearing before the altitude listener can function correctly. This second pair of trumpets takes the place of hypothetical ears mounted on the crown of the head and under the chin, and the corresponding directional listening operation would be analogous to the nodding of the head after it has been swung round to face the sound.

In 1923, the Acoustical Section of the Air Defence Experimental Establishment (Biggin Hill) had the problem of producing a portable sound locator which could be packed in a case after dismantling. The base length of 4 ft. 6 in. was used, but the horns were made smaller than in the early British pattern and, being metal-lined, withstood damage, for a fine crack in a wooden horn of the early type kills its magnifying properties. The performance of this locator after training was adequate for the slow moving and heavy bombing aircraft of ten years ago, but, owing to the high speed of modern aircraft, it is gradually losing its usefulness.

This magnification produced by horns is helpful because it reduces the reaction time of the listener; hence he gets on the correct bearing more quickly than if he were dealing with faint sounds. The horns, however, have another property which helps the listener. As they are rotated into the true direction, the intensity increases, and the listener will naturally turn the horn so that the sound is loudest. High-pitched sounds are more strongly magnified than the low-pitched sounds. The intensity variation as the horn rotates is also greater for the high-pitched sounds. We do not hear the aeroplane through the horns exactly as we hear it with the unaided ear, and, as we rotate them, the quality of sound changes, being richest when the horns face the sound.

We get, then, three factors affecting our correct estimate of direction - the binaural sense which depends on time difference, giving us the sense of sound straight ahead when facing it, the intensity of the sound which becomes greater, and the quality of the sound which becomes richer and more closely resembles that of the aeroplane as heard by the unaided ear.

Of recent years, several well-known armament firms have produced sound locators in which great diversity of design has been exhibited. Sound collectors have been either of the horn type or have employed concave reflectors with special devices for conveying the sound to the ears. A modern example of the horn type is that produced by Sperry in the United States. Another type, produced by the firm of Barbier, Benard and Turenne, provides collectors each one of which is composed of a number of horns connected at their narrow ends. The Sautter Harle locator, also produced in France, is of the reflector type, and so also is one produced by the firm of Goerz of Vienna, in which many striking acoustical features are introduced.

The Sperry sound locator consists of large exponential horns, that is horns with curved sides in which the cross-section diminishes in logarithmic relation with distance from the mouth. As such they accord with the latest scientific principles and, in fact, lend themselves to calculation both as regards frequency response and frequency range. They are 16 ft. long and give a base length of 7 ft. The listeners are, as it were, clamped to the horns by caps carrying earpads through which sound has access to the ear. They give an impressive magnification, but, unfortunately, are extremely resonant and, in even light winds, provide a disturbing background which hampers listening. This difficulty is overcome by a prolonged period of training. A feature of the trumpet which is liable to be overlooked is the danger to the listener of local gun sounds in which the gun blast is greatly concentrated. These Sperry locators (below), in the hands of trained troops, give a good performance.

By the way of comparison, the latest British sound locator is shown (overleaf). Collectors which are paraboloid reflectors have been evolved as the result of researches in which the acoustical properties are accurately known. As in the best of the Continental locators, the instrument is trailer-mounted and the listeners adjust the positions of the locator and themselves by hand-wheel control. The instrument is highly directional, is free from trumpet resonance and can be used in moderately noisy surroundings. In general, a condition of absolute silence is imposed in the neighbourhood of these locators while they are in operation, but with the new English locator it is quite possible to do effective work when onlookers are talking near it, so long as they keep away from the direction of listening.

Reviewing all these types of locator, it is interesting to note that, working on independent lines, the mouths of the collectors, which is an important feature of selective directional listening, and the length of the base between collectors, which determines accuracy of location, have achieved about equal dimensions throughout, but it must be confessed that some of the designs do not accord with the simplicity of the functions which they have to carry out.

Efforts of various countries have been concentrated hitherto on the production of sound locators in which the ear is the ultimate criterion. Directive listening is known to require training, and a certain proportion of military and civil personnel are quite incapable of being trained. The British locator has proved itself to be a very rapid

training instrument, but with all possible improvements, some listeners are physically incapable of good performance.

More recently, however, attention has been directed to the production of electrical locators in which it is hoped that difficulties of training will, to some extent, be eliminated.

It is only during the last year that microphones in Great Britain have been produced for all round listening which can be matched as accurately as the ears are matched. The sensitivity of the microphones themselves is inadequate, and they must have amplifiers similar to wireless amplifiers, but of special design. These again must be matched, or they will, of themselves, introduce time errors or, better expressed, phase changes. Also, the power of discrimination of wanted from unwanted sounds, used automatically by the ears of the listener, must find its analogy in some electrical device, and recently we have been able to produce electrical filters which help to cut out the sounds which form an undesired background.

Finally, we should naturally replace the stethoscopes by telephones, which again must be matched, but that leads us back again to the ear with all its inherent difficulties. There

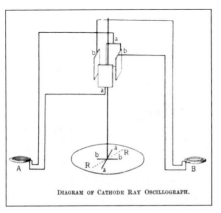

DIAGRAM OF CATHODE RAY OSCILLOGRAPH.

is, however, an alternative to the ear in the cathode ray oscillograph, which may be used in a manner suggested by Dr ET Paris. We have two receptors, so to speak, in the two pairs of parallel plates in the oscillograph, and the two microphone circuits may be connected to these so that each microphone effect can be recorded as a corresponding movement of the spot on the screen. Fig. 3 shows diagrammatically the four plates of the oscillograph, in which plates aa correspond to microphone A and plates bb to microphone B. The displacements aa and bb on the screen shown below correspond to their separate movements. These movements which are, of course, oscillatory, give by persistence of vision a straight line for each microphone, but when the two microphones are connected up, we get the well-known Lissajou figure, which would be another straight line equally inclined to the first two if these two microphone responses are in phase. When out of phase, the effect depends on the nature of the sound. If the sound is a pure musical tone, re-presented by a sine wave form, the intervening out-of-phase conditions are represented by ellipses. If, however, the source of sound is as complex as that of an aircraft, and is built up of many frequencies, the pattern only becomes simple, that is, the straight line above referred to, if all the constituents are in phase, namely, when the microphones are equidistant from the source.

Gusty winds make directional listening very difficult; for the critical time difference on which direction finding depends becomes variable. The cathode ray oscillograph gives a perfect picture of this disability. The straight line then becomes blurred, and if the sound intensities change, as they do in the two receivers, at unequal rates, the resultant line oscillates. The aural and visual perceptions give an exact parallel. Similarly, other sources of sound, or, it may be reflections of the same source, confuse both aural and visual effects equally. This method of visual indication by the cathode ray oscillograph gives immediate evidence of listening disabilities.

I have so far dealt with sound direction finders in which the two ears or their equivalents in microphones are necessary. There are, however, direction finders in which use is made of single collectors which can rotate to face the sound and so find a maximum of intensity. Although these direction finders are of considerable interest, they fail to give the accuracy shown by the binaural instruments, and, furthermore, present difficulties in recovering the direction of the sound when it is lost.

I will only give one example of this type, which is of interest in so far as it is entirely devoted to peace operations, and deals with the direction finding of fog horns and ships' sirens at sea. The need of supplementing the human ear has been recognized by many navigators, especially as meteorological conditions sometimes baffle the listeners. Situations may also arise when the nearness of the foghorn involves hasty and definite action. The invention of Messrs W & TG Hodgkinson is directed to the supply of accurate bearings (to half a point of the compass).

The devices tried out were of two types. The first and simpler form of direction finder consisted of a paraboloidal receiver mounted in a drum rotatable about a vertical axis. The axis of the paraboloid was horizontal and coincided with a diameter of the drum. At the focus of the paraboloid a contact microphone was mounted, and the mouth of the paraboloid was protected from wind by a perforated screen. Microphone adjustments were such that the noises of the ship on which it was erected and disturbances from wind produced little effect, but it would respond to horns and sirens up to ranges of three miles. The axis of the drum carried a commutator, and brushes were arranged so that, for sixteen positions of the drum, currents generated by sound in the microphone could light a lamp through the agency of a relay. Sixteen of these lamps were arranged in a dial to give the points of the compass against which any sound disturbance could be anticipated. For near foghorns, a group of lights might be shown on a definite arc, the centre of which would give the bearing. This Instrument was used for a period on the Mersey pilot-service and on the Holyhead - Dublin mail Service. A later pattern, where a much larger drum was used, avoided the operation of rotating the drum, the same effect being achieved by using a number of radial paraboloid receivers, each with its own light indicator. This was installed on SS Victorian of the Allan Line on the Liverpool - Montreal service. The instrument, though successful, was not brought into general use.

It may be suggested that considerable gain might be achieved by using very large receivers. This development, however, has not been pursued because it has been discovered that appreciable increase in acoustical range has not been comparable - a result which can be attributed to the very high attenuation of sound in the atmosphere. The application of the inverse square law is not helpful in estimating range extension, since, at greater distances than normal listening, the attenuation losses are high in comparison with those due to spherical divergence. Very large receivers have been tried and have resulted in very disappointing performance at long ranges. Thus, large exponential horns which admittedly magnify very impressively, will add only a few miles to the audible range. A gain in accuracy of direction finding may be achieved, but, even so, the accuracy obtained by a single large receiver working on a maximum of intensity cannot compete with that derived by employing the binaural effect, using pairs of receivers of more modest dimensions.

It is obvious that no description of sound direction finding would be adequate without reference to two sources of error. The first one, which applies to the location of all sources of sound, whether fixed or moving, is due to the physical nature of the atmosphere. The effect of wind in creating difficulties of listening range is, of course, familiar, and I do not wish to dwell on this. Meteorological acoustics is a science of itself and might easily occupy the whole of this discourse. It is my purpose rather to indicate in a few words how wind and temperature may affect the direction of listening. We may regard the velocity of sound in still air at uniform temperature as a physical constant, but air is very rarely still and never at a fixed temperature as we ascend. We must increase or decrease the velocity of sound according as the wind is with or against the direction of travel, and according as the temperature increases or decreases. The effect of the variation is to produce refraction, to a greater or less degree, and the effects of these variations have been worked out precisely from mathematical considerations[5]. The following simple illustrations indicate in what manner meteorological conditions affect directional listening. If we consider the wind to increase with height in the direction of listening, the sound ray comes down more steeply. If opposite to the direction of listening, the sound ray is bent so that it comes in at a smaller angle. For example, in south-west wind so prevalent in England, an aeroplane would be heard in a south-west direction at a higher angle than the true, or, if with the same wind we listen to an aeroplane in the north-east, we should be hearing it at a lower angle. The reason is that wind from the south-west increases as we ascend in nearly all cases.

The effect of the temperature is such that, if no wind had to be allowed for, the aeroplane would always be heard at a lower angle of elevation than it actually is. The reason is that the temperature during the day is nearly always lower as we ascend, and, in consequence, the velocity decreases. The effect is the same as if we were listening against the wind, as described above. At night, however, the reverse effect frequently occurs, because the ground cools by radiation and the temperature of the air above it is higher. At night therefore it frequently happens that we hear an aeroplane at a greater angle of elevation. These effects are quite large, as much as 10° for very low angles of elevation, but when the aeroplane approaches the over-head position, these errors become negligible. An illustration is shown in Fig. 4, where the directions of sound rays given out by an aeroplane at 7,000 ft. are mapped out. This acoustical distribution of rays can be worked out if we know how wind and temperature change as we ascend. Here, the sound rays spread in such a way as to give a region in which no sound is heard, hence no direction can be defined; but above and below it there are errors in direction as shown. Provision for such corrections will eventually be made, for, if sound is to be employed for controlling gun fire, great accuracy will be essential in obtaining direction.

The survey of the atmosphere as regards wind and temperature has been accessory to a large research (now being carried out by P. Rothwell) on the refraction of sound in the atmosphere.

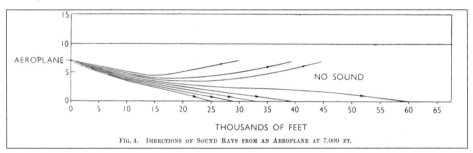

FIG. 4. DIRECTIONS OF SOUND RAYS FROM AN AEROPLANE AT 7,000 FT.

A more serious error in sound direction finding occurs if the source of sound is moving. The small velocity of sound relative to that of light is responsible for an error called the 'lag of sound', and it can be defined as the angle between the line of sight and the direction of listening. Taking an aeroplane as the moving source, while the sound which it gives out is approaching the listener, the aeroplane has travelled on its course, so that the listening direction will always be behind the visual one. The lag of sound varies according to the direction in which we are listening. If the aeroplane is coming straight towards us or receding from us, there is no correction; but if it is flying across our field of vision, such as it would be if vertically overhead, the lag of sound is a maximum. The angle thus becomes approximately $\varphi = v/F$ where V is the speed of sound and v the air-speed of the target, but a wind correction must be incorporated with this if the wind varies between the aeroplane and the ground. No correction is necessary if there is no wind. How large the correction may be is indicated in the accompanying table, which gives the angular lag of listening direction for an aircraft flying overhead. Against this correction, a year is quoted, corresponding roughly to the speeds of aircraft prevalent at that time.

The corrections would suggest a very serious disability in sound locating, but this disability may easily be exaggerated, for, if we know the airspeed of the aircraft and the direction in which it is travelling, corrections may be applied with considerable precision. The various sound locators have devices attached to them which insert the lag of sound corrections and, in some cases, corrections for wind and temperature refraction.

	Air speed : miles per hour	Angular error overhead position
1918	60	4·6°
1926	120	9·1°
1934	180	13·8°
1936	240	18·4°
1940?	300	23·0°

We must, of course, remember that acoustical direction finding cannot compete with the precisions of visual observations, but it is not too much to say that, on fixed sources of sound, an error of ¼ degree be assured with the modern Instruments, and with an aeroplane flying at reasonable heights, all sound locator manufacturers quote 2° accuracy. The distance away of the target is, of course, a determining factor, as with low-flying targets having a high angular velocity, difficulties of following, both physical and psychological, make the operation of direction finding difficult. By careful training, a listening team of two listeners per locator can achieve an accuracy of 1° for a reasonable proportion of the time during which the aircraft is within hearing and at heights above 5,000 ft.

Is sound as an aid to defence likely to be completely outclassed because of its low velocity? We are apt, with the sensational reports of greater and greater speeds of aircraft, to exaggerate the heavy handicaps from which sound suffers. In direction finding, it is true that a large correction may be involved, but, if it is an accurate one, the result may still be adequate for the purpose for which sound locators were designed. We are by no means approaching yet the stage described in the well-known petrol advertisement, and we have one consolation in the fact that very high-speed aircraft produce much stronger sounds than those flying at lower speeds, so that what we lose in time through high speed we gain in range of audibility.

It is not desired, however, to close on the note of war. We are endowed with a directional listening faculty, the study of which has been seriously neglected. We scarcely appreciated that we had this faculty until sound locators were designed and time differences exaggerated, so that an almost uncanny throwing of our perception of sound from one ear to the other was observed only by a slight rotation of such instruments.

We have claimed the impulsive character of the aircraft sound as a valuable asset in sound direction finding, and we have been able to explain the phenomenon of direction listening on the time difference theory of Hornbostel. It has, however, been the subject of psychological researches to try if sense of direction is lost when the sounds are pure tones. Banister[6] has by suitable laboratory equipment tested certain observers on pure tones and has come to the conclusion that tones of frequency ranging from 133 cycles to 1,705 cycles can give a binaural effect and that discrete impulses are not essential. Our own experience is that lower frequency pure tones are very difficult to locate.

Banister has attempted to reconcile these results with Hornbostel's theory of time differences and has produced a theory which may explain why such an operation is possible. The crests of the sound wave, so to speak, can fulfil the function of discrete pulses, if certain assumptions are made on the mechanism of the ear.

These and other experiments on the theories of hearing should benefit by the attention now being devoted to sound direction finding, and it is hoped that instruments devised specifically to defend us against war dangers will thus give an impetus to work of purely scientific value.

1 J. Hegen, *Sitz. Akad. Wiss. Wien, Math.-Naturwiss. KL,* (1), 132, 81 (1924).
2 Engelmann, *'Untersuchungen über die Schall-lokalisation bei Thieren'.* (JA Barth, Leipzig.)
3 E.M von Hornbostel. 'The Time Theory of Sound-Localization'. Physical Society Discussion on Audition, June 19, 1931.
4 'Dictionary of Applied Physics', vol. 4, p. 733.
5 BA Milne. 'Sound Waves in the Atmosphere'. Phil. Mag., 42, 100 (1921). Tucker. 'Some Problems of Modern Meteorology. No. 11 Meteorological Acoustics'.Quart. J. Roy. Met. Soc., 59, No. 250, July, 1933.
6 H Banister. 'The Basis of Sound-Localization'. Physical Society Discussion on Audition, June 19, 1931.

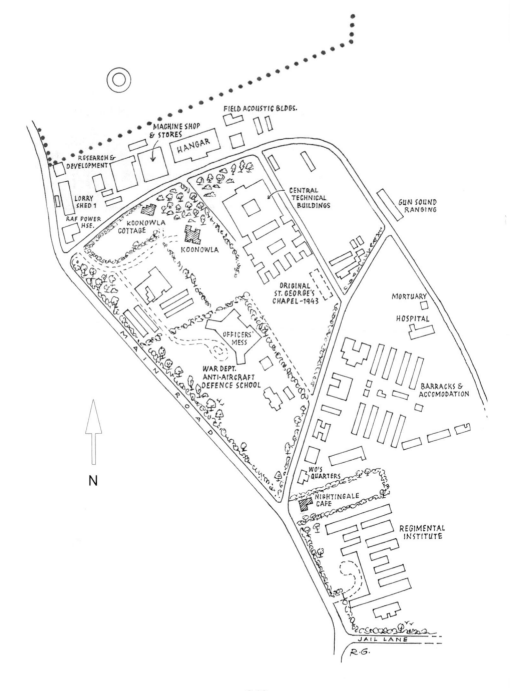

FIELD ACOUSTIC BLDGS.

MACHINE SHOP
& STORES

HANGAR

RESEARCH &
DEVELOPMENT

LORRY
SHED 1

RAF POWER
HSE.

KOONOWLA
COTTAGE

KOONOWLA

CENTRAL
TECHNICAL
BUILDINGS

GUN SOUND
RANGING

ORIGINAL
ST. GEORGE'S
CHAPEL - 1943

MORTUARY

HOSPITAL

OFFICERS'
MESS

WAR DEPT.
ANTI-AIRCRAFT
DEFENCE SCHOOL

BARRACKS &
ACCOMODATION

M A I N   R O A D

N

WO'S
QUARTERS

NIGHTINGALE
CAFE

REGIMENTAL
INSTITUTE

JAIL LANE

R.G.

South Camp - the War Department site in 1941. Much of the original camp is still in place but new building is going on in the centre.

BEST SELLING BOOK ON THE BATTLE OF BRITAIN FROM THE GERMAN SIDE. NOW ALSO AVAILABLE IN PAPERBACK

SPITFIRE ON MY TAIL

On 27 October 1940, having completed over 150 missions, Oberleutnant Ulrich Steinhilper's fighter was shot down, crashing into the Kent countryside near Canterbury. For Ulrich that was the end of everything for which he'd been prepared in the Luftwaffe since his acceptance in 1936. But there is more than a pilot's story to tell. He shares with the reader what it was like to grow up in Germany as the crippling conditions of the Treaty of Versailles bled away the country's economy; how it was inevitable that the people would succumb to the fatal attraction of Hitler and 'The Party'. More personally, Ulrich relates how the intrigues and politics of a small town were to shape his destiny.

From a mountain village in southern Germany to Berlin swollen with people for the 1936 Olympic Games, we follow Ulrich to the start of his military career and through the rigorous basic training to his first faltering flights as a pilot. Onwards, towards the Battle of Britain and his uncompromising views of the conduct of the battle both by the Luftwaffe High Command and the RAF.

In a fighter group decimated by losses and battle fatigue Ulrich still carries on, but is he really prepared for what has befallen his friends and colleagues? If the Luftwaffe's estimates of British fighter strength were correct, then why are they still facing such determined resistance? Will the Army ever start the invasion of Britain? Will the sacrifice of so many airmen have been for nothing?

Foreword by Stephen Bungay – Author of 'Most Dangerous Enemy'

Hardback:ISBN (13) 978-1-872836-00-3
384 pages, hardback
240 mm x 160 mm
Over eighty b&w photographs.

Price: **£19.95**

SPITFIRE ON MY TAIL

Large Format Paperback

The paperback option of Steinhilper's classic work.

Paperback: ISBN (13): 978-1-872836-79-9

384 pages, paperback

240 mm x 160 mm

Over eighty b&w photographs.

Price: **£12.95**

TEN MINUTES TO BUFFALO

The Story of Germany's Great Escaper
Ulrich Steinhilper & Peter Osborne

Non-Fiction Illustrated

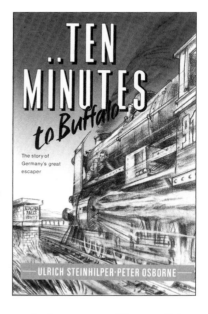

'Ten Minutes to Buffalo' is the sequel to Ulrich Steinhilper's highly successful first book, 'Spitfire On My Tail'. Unlike the first book, which tells the story of how a young German came to fly in Hitler's Luftwaffe and to fight in the Battle of Britain, 'Ten Minutes to Buffalo' is a catalogue of courage and determination on the ground. In this way it is set to repeat the successful formula by providing a rare chance to witness how things were for 'The Other Side,' this time behind the barbed wire and in Ulrich Steinhilper's case - all too often outside the wire! It relates a story of remarkable courage and perseverance in the most appalling conditions, braving arctic weather and appalling hardship with one thought in mind - to get home.

From his first camp in England away to the vastness of Canada, he and a select few of his fellow officers were to become known as *Die Ausbrecherkönige von Kanada* (the breakout kings from Canada) and Ulrich was to shine among them. His escapes were innovative and even audacious and it was only bad luck that seemed to keep him from a completely successful 'homerun'.

Very little has ever been written about the conditions of German officers as prisoners of the Allies and practically nothing of their ingenuity and perseverance in planning and executing escape plans so similar to their counterparts in German hands. This remarkable book is entirely written from original hand-written sheets which date from 1942 and which give it a great immediacy and accuracy.
ISBN (13)978-1-872836-01-0

Hardback only, 431 pages, 45 black & white illustrations. 240 mm x 160 mm

Price: £14.95

FULL CIRCLE

The Long Way Home From Canada
Ulrich Steinhilper & Peter Osborne

'Full Circle' is the last of three books which record Ulrich Steinhilper's remarkable experiences in the Second World War. From being a front line fighter pilot in the Battle of Britain he becomes a Prisoner of War, but for Ulrich the war is far from over.

   In 'Ten Minutes To Buffalo', the story of the first three escapes is told and in 'Full Circle' the story is continued as Ulrich and Hinnerk Waller find themselves back in custody. But that is far from the end of Ulrich's career as an escaper. Nor is it the end of the detailed and fascinating description of life as a POW. Locking up large numbers of bright young men led to the most ingenious schemes to manufacture their own radios, make their own tools and later, on their Ehrenwort (word of honour), to rebuild and run a farm.

   Ulrich describes in graphic detail his last attempt to get back to Germany, admitting it was the worst mistake he ever made in his life. From documents, hand-written at the time, and from numerous letters and postcards home he accurately reconstructs what it was like to be a prisoner of the Allies and the hardships that brought at the end.

   'Full Circle' completes Ulrich Steinhilper's odyssey and, with, it what is now being described as one of the most important contributions to the broader history of the Second World War to emerge in recent times.

Non-Fiction Illustrated

ISBN (13) 978-1-872836-02-7

Hardback only, 408 pages, 74 black & white pictures and illustrations. 240 mm x 160 mm

Price: £17.95

DON'T TALK – DO IT   Ulrich Steinhilper

Word Processing is a term which most people understand today, but fifty years ago there was only one voice using it, a young typewriter sales-man who was working for IBM Germany. Ulrich Steinhilper had the idea to use Textverarbeitung (Word Processing), a new concept, so that office products could be marketed in the same way that Data Processing equipment was sold by IBM. It was not as we might recognise it today; it was more a holistic approach to the diverse skills which are needed to improve office efficiency and to bring streamlined factory production line techniques to the office. Fortunately he submit-ted his thoughts as a Staff Suggestion and was duly paid 25 German Marks for his trouble, but he had registered it and had proof of it. When others tried to claim that it was they who had first conceived the name 'Word Processing' Ul-rich fought for recognition and, finally, IBM committed it to paper and sent him on a trip around the world in recognition of his work. Over and above being the story of the evolution of Word Processing, 'Don't Talk - Do It!' is a fascinating record of the development of post-war business. It is also an intriguing illustration of how one man made his contribution in the true pioneering spirit, helping Germany rise from the ruins of World War II to one of the world's most successful industrial nations.

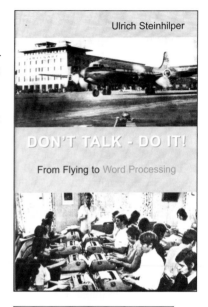

Non-Fiction Illustrated.
ISBN (13) 978 1 872836 75 1

Hardback only, 272 pages, 40 black & white pictures and illustrations. 240 mm x 160 mm   **Price: 16.95**

TARGET DRESDEN

Alan Cooper

On the night of 13-14th February 1945, 796
Lancasters and 9 Mosquitoes of RAF Bomber
Command, dropped 1,478 tons of high explosive
and 1,182 tons of incendiaries on the city of
Dresden. A firestorm developed, which led to
large areas of the city being burned out. At the
time of the attack, Dresden was crowded with
refugees fleeing the advancing Soviet Army resulting in between 40,000 and 50,000 casualties.
On the morning of the 14th a second attack was
carried out by the United States Army Air Force
followed by two further US attacks.
Target Dresden chronicles the development of
bombing from the earliest days through the tactical and strategic bombing of WWII and gives
the story behind these controversial raids.

Non-Fiction Illustrated

ISBN (13): 978-1-872836-60-7

Paperback: 256 pages, 43 b&w photographs and illustrations. 240 mm x 160 mm

Price: £9.95

TEST PILOTS

Wolfgang Späte

This is an exciting book relating the firsthand experiences of predominantly German Test Pilots. Including over one hundred photographs and illustrations, the majority of which have never been seen before, it is full of refreshingly new material.

The collection of anecdotal accounts covers such varied flying tests as those of the Natter, a manned, rocket-launched interceptor designed to release a salvo of missiles at Flying Fortress formations; and the DFS 228, arguably the forerunner of the Lockheed U2, with a service ceiling calculated at eighty thousand feet and a range of nearly a thousand miles. There are also vivid descriptions of the first trials of the ejector seat; towing aircraft on a one metre long rigid tow; the beginnings of air-to-air refuelling, and even the plans for a bomber which would tow its own fighter escort across the Atlantic to engage the USAF over their home ground. Test Pilots is essential reading for all aviation enthusiasts and historians.

Foreword by Captain Eric 'Winkle' Brown
C.O. Enemy Aircraft Flight, RAE Farnborough (1945–47)
Author of 'Wings On My Sleeve'

'Although Wolfgang Späte never became an established test pilot himself, he has opened the door into some fascinating scenarios which caught his imagination. The reader should eagerly share these.'

Captain Eric Brown, CBE, DSC, AFC, RN

Non-Fiction Illustrated. ISBN (13) 978-1-872836-80-5
Paperback: 304 pages 102 b&w photographs. 240 mm x 160 mm
and illustrations.

Price: £9.95

BLUE SKIES AND DARK NIGHTS

Bill Randle

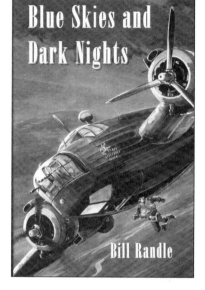

'Blue Skies and Dark Nights' is the autobiography of Group Captain Bill Randle. From his initial flight training in the United States on the fledgling Arnold scheme, to the bombing of Germany, through a remarkable evasion and successful 'home run', to MI9 and the formation of post-war Escape and Evasion policy with the Americans, to learning to fly helicopters with the US Marines, then on to taking part in search and rescue missions in Korea; this is a honest and straightforward account of a unusual career in the RAF and beyond.

Those with an interest in the RAF and world affairs will find Bill Randle's story fascinating as he describes what it was like to be at the centre of many world events. It also clearly illustrates the frustrations implicit in a service life, as well as the great humour and tragedy which go with the acceptance of the responsibilities of rank.

Non-Fiction Illustrated

ISBN (13): 978-1-872836-40-9

Hardback only, 352 pages, iillustrated with over 90 black & white photographs.
240 mm x 160 mm

Price: £9.95

MY WAR

Behind Enemy Lines with SOE
in Europe and the Far East

Harry Verlander

The Special Operations Executive (SOE) French
section, Jedburgh teams, and Special Air Service
(SAS) sent into west and south-west France,
helped the French Resistance liberate the whole
area without assistance from any other ground
forces.

Having been deeply involved behind the lines in
France, Harry Verlander volunteered to serve
once more, but this time in the mountains and
jungles of Burma. No more the rolling countryside of rural France but the brutal uncompromising hand-to-hand fighting against the Japanese.
This very personal story gives a detailed account of both the campaign in France and that
vicious time in Burma.

ISBN: 9781872836850
Hardback 368 pages. Over 80 b&w photographs and illustrations.
240mm x 160mm

Price: £19.95

SHARK SQUADRON PILOT

Bert Horden

A graphic illustration of the realities of the air
war in the Western Desert, Shark Squadron Pilot
describes Bert Horden's service with 112 'Shark'
Squadron and the ground attack role of the
'Kittys'. With their garish shark's mouths
painted on their aircraft 112 Squadron wreaked
havoc on the German Afrika Korps inflicting
terrible damage with machine gun fire and
under-slung bombs.

Using his diary and flying log book to preserve
the accuracy and immediacy of the events Bert
Horden presents a superbly graphic account of
desert flying.

ISBN: 9781872836454
Hardback. 193 Pages. Over 80 b&w photographs
240mm x 160mm

Price: £9.95

ECHOES FROM THE SKY
Richard Scarth

The preeminent book on acoustic location has been reprinted as is available from:

The Hythe Society:
treasurer@hythecivicsociety.org.
Alan Joyce, 6 London Road , Hythe ,Kent CT21 4DF .
The cost of the book is £8.50 , of which £1 is donated to the Romney Marsh Countryside Project , who managed the Mirrors at Denge,nr Dungeness . Uk postal cost is £1.70 making a total of £10.20
Highly recommended

No. 32 Squadron Hurricane flown by Peter Brothers from
RAF BIGGIN HILL
1940

BARRY WEEKLY
Aviation Art

For a superb choice of original aviation art you are invited to visit Barry Weekley's web page:

http://www.barryweekleyart.com